PRACTICAL ELECTRONICS
FOR RAILWAY MODELLERS
2

PRACTICAL ELECTRONICS
FOR RAILWAY MODELLERS
2

Roger Amos

Patrick Stephens, Wellingborough

WARNING!
ELECTRICITY CAN BE DANGEROUS!
The electronic projects in this book are, to
the best of the author's knowledge and belief,
both accurately described and safe. However,
great care must always be taken when
assembling electronic circuits, and neither the
publishers nor the author can accept
responsibility for any accidents which may
occur.

First published in 1985

British Library Cataloguing in Publication Data

Amos, Roger
    Practical electronics for railway modellers.
    2
    1. Railroads—Models—Electronic equipment
    I. Title
    625.1'9   TF197

    ISBN 0-85059-709-9

*Patrick Stephens Limited is part of the
Thorsons Publishing Group.*

Photoset in 10 on 11 pt Times by MJL
Typesetting, Hitchin, Herts. Printed in Great
Britain on New Edition Book Wove Vol 17.5
80 gsm, and bound, by Woolnough
Bookbinding, Wellingborough, Northants, for
the publishers, Patrick Stephens Limited,
Denington Estate, Wellingborough, Northants,
NN8 2QD, England.

Contents

Part 4   Signalling systems

Part 5   Automatic train control projects

Part 6   Train lighting systems

Introduction and acknowledgements

Railway modellers are, of necessity, people who like to see things *move.* Perhaps this is why they are happy to use switches and relays galore, both of which have moving parts, but generally fight shy of using electronic circuitry which would do the same job more cheaply and reliably, but which lacks moving parts.

My first book, *Practical Electronics for Railway Modellers,* published by Patrick Stephens Ltd in 1982, described 31 projects of varying complexity, starting with some very simple introductory circuits. Appendices at the end of the book introduced readers to such practical considerations as soldering, the resistor/capacitor colour code and some of the very useful theory behind electronics, eg Ohm's law. The book was intended for railway modellers who had little or no previous experience of electronics.

Practical Electronics for Railway Modellers was well received and its sales showed that it did indeed fill a gap in the market. This led the publishers to ask me for a sequel. This I was happy to do for a number of reasons: (i) None of the projects in the first book used integrated circuits (ICs). This was for two reasons. One was a desire to keep everything as simple as possible for the benefit of readers who were newcomers to electronics. The other was, as I stated in the Introduction to that book, that in my first five years of model railway electronics experience I had never found an IC that was useful. Neither of these reasons apply now, so consequently most of the circuits in *this* book do use ICs. (ii) Since I finished writing *Practical Electronics for Railway Modellers,* I have continued experimenting, especially in the fields of track circuiting and signalling. Inevitably I have learned a lot more about these and I had contemplated writing a specialist book on the subject, but its appeal would have been limited so all the circuits from that proposed book have been incorporated into this one. (iii) When I wrote *Practical Electronics for Railway Modellers* I was unfamiliar with two American books on the subject, *Model Railroad Electronics* by James Kyle and *Practical Electronic Projects for Model Railroaders* by P.J. Thorne. My attention was drawn to these only just in time to refer to them in the final 'further reading' appendix. While I have not copied any circuits from either book, reading them has inevitably given me a number of ideas and, also, has clarified my understanding of some subjects. This led to a number of new circuit ideas. (iv) Electronics is a scene of rapid technological development. Any book on electronics is out of date before it even leaves the press! Since writing my first book there have been many new developments, especially in LED (light emitting diode) technology, which are of immediate relevance to railway modellers.

So, the way was prepared for this book which assumes some familiarity with electronics. Readers having no prior knowledge should consult the relevant sections of my first book, while readers who are familiar with electronics, but unfamiliar with my first book, will nevertheless find a comprehensive selection of model railway electronic projects in this volume.

Much the same sequence has been followed as before. Part 1 is concerned with controllers and includes four contrasting circuits, three using ICs, while Part 2 discusses accessories for controllers, including a fascinating speedometer. Part 3 is devoted to track circuiting systems with five different types of track circuit unit being described. Units for both live-rail and return-rail monitoring are included and all the units on a layout may share the same power supply, irrespective of the number of controllers in use. This eliminates some of the complications experienced with earlier systems. Part 4 provides a more complete range of signalling circuits than in *Practical Electronics for Railway Modellers*. Two-, three- and four-aspect drivers for multi-lens and searchlight-type signals are given and the 74/74LS series of transistor/transistor logic (TTL) ICs are used throughout. A simple capacitor charge/discharge unit for driving point or semaphore signal motors incorporates a logic output for the signalling system. One chapter shows how a hybrid TTL/LED device can be used to make an effective 'theatre'-type route indicator. Part 5 is a departure from the sequence of my first book. In this section a diversity of projects are grouped that take an input from a track circuit or the signalling system and which are then used to control the train in some way. An example of this is a highly improved version of the capacitor slow-down circuit which was first shown in *Practical Electronics for Railway Modellers*. Another example is a more sophisticated interlock for stopping trains at danger signals and a timer circuit is included for automatic station stops. Two chapters describe methods for simultaneously controlling a number of trains on a conventionally wired layout; the second of which, *Progressive cab control,* is a sophisticated system incorporating a comprehensive interlock network. Part 6 is concerned with train lighting, two contrasting systems being described, while Part 7 is about sound effects and methods of reproducing them on board a moving model train. A final set of appendices cover fault finding, TTL and the characteristics of two popular linear ICs.

However, this book is certainly not the last word on the subject for that can only be written after the last electronic device has been invented! And there must be many, many more applications for the devices mentioned in this book, and for other devices currently available. For further projects readers are recommended to the quarterly magazine *Model Railway Electronics* (Dalkeith Publishing Ltd).

Finally, I must acknowledge my gratitude to many organisations and persons for their assistance in the preparation of this book. I name especially Westinghouse Signals Ltd for information on prototype signalling systems, Maplin Electronic Supplies Ltd for permission to reproduce TTL pinouts from their catalogue and RCA Corporation for permission to reproduce the information found in Appendices 6 and 7 of this book.

I owe an incalculable debt to my father, S.W. Amos, who nurtured my interest in electronics from an early age and is still a source of the most helpful criticism and advice. Finally, and by no means least, I salute my long-suffering wife, Jennifer, who has endured unreasonable desertion while I have been 'playing with trains and wires' in preparation for this book.

Roger S. Amos
Rugby
October 1984

Controllers

Introduction

The function of a controller (or 'throttle', as it is called in North America) is to regulate the speed and direction of a model train. Electronics make precise control possible, since a transistor is a device for the accurate and efficient control of electric current.

Electronic controllers fall into two categories. In a *closed-loop* controller the circuit compares the voltage across the locomotive motor with a control voltage set by the speed control. Any potential deviation in speed arising from a change in voltage across the motor (due to a variety of reasons) is prevented by the closed-loop controller which automatically introduces compensation, thus holding the speed steady. In a *pulse-width modulation* (PWM) controller, the output consists of pulses of full power and speed is controlled by adjusting the length of the pulses; for low speeds the pulses are kept brief, while for higher speeds the pulses are longer and the spaces between them correspondingly shorter. A PWM controller may incorporate the kind of feedback-loop found in a closed-loop controller and a closed-loop controller may well, by using an unsmoothed power supply, deliver a pulsed output, which assists in smooth starts. Four circuits for controllers are given in this section: two closed-loop types and two PWM.

Chapter 1 shows a basic closed-loop controller, having only six components (including the reversing switch, but excluding the power supply). An ideal first project, it nevertheless gives such outstanding performance that it has become a 'standard' on the author's layout. It also introduces readers to the concept of the integrated circuit. Chapter 2 shows a more complex closed-loop controller using the 741 operational amplifier IC, while in Chapter 3 is a PWM controller, using the 555 timer IC as a pulse generator.

Finally, Chapter 4 describes a controller that is unique in this section in that it uses discrete components (that is not ICs) throughout and is a sophisticated circuit embodying both PWM and closed-loop techniques.

Chapter 1: Basic closed-loop controller

This controller, which uses only six components (excluding those in the power supply), originated by accident when I was adapting a sophisticated cassette-

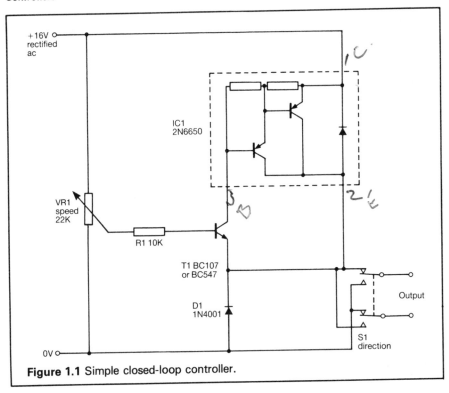

Figure 1.1 Simple closed-loop controller.

recorder motor control for model railway use. This circuit used the 723 voltage regulator IC with a 2N6650 power Darlington as its output stage. It worked quite well for a while and then failed. Investigation showed that the 723 IC had 'burned out' although used well within its limits. To test the 2N6650 for damage I connected its base direct to the speed control potentiometer. The resulting simple controller performed even better than that using the 723! A few refinements, such as a T1, led to the circuit shown in Figure 1.1.

Generally, this controller is similar to Project 7 in *Practical Electronics for Railway Modellers,* the main difference being that 100 per cent negative feedback is applied with the output being returned direct to the emitter of T1. This transistor, therefore, is used as a comparator — it compares the output voltage (on its emitter) with the control voltage (on its base). Under normal conditions resistor R1 is unnecessary, but is included to protect T1's base/emitter junction against burn-out if the controller output should be short-circuited while the speed control is at maximum. The value of R1, like that of VR1, is uncritical. The nature of the feedback-loop ensures that the base/emitter junction of T1 is normally nearly reverse biased; consequently, the input resistance on the base of T1 is very high. This makes this controller ideal for use with voltage-control systems such as Project 13 in *Practical Electronics for Railway Modellers* and those in Chapters 5 and 6 of this book.

The diode D1 protects the base/emitter junction of T1 against inductive overshoot. Its omission would make it difficult to stop certain types of locomotive.

IC1 resembles an ordinary power transistor both in appearance and function but it is, strictly speaking, an integrated circuit incorporating in one 'chip' of silicon two pnp transistors in Darlington configuration, two bypass ('pull-up') resistors to ensure that the Darlington turns fully off when unbiased and a diode which provides additional protection from inductive effects. The overall current gain of the 2N6650 is of the order of 10,000. If you cannot obtain (or afford) a 2N6650, you could use two discrete transistors instead, eg a BC557 followed by an MJE 2955. Connect a 1K resistor between base and emitter of the first and a 100 Ω between base and emitter of the second.

Power supply

You should use a full-wave rectified AC supply giving an indicated 16 V DC. The outputs obtained from many commercial power supplies are ideal. Lower voltages or half-wave rectified AC will give reduced power. If a *smoothed* supply is used, much of the controllability at low speeds will be lost and gentle starts may be impossible. The power supply must incorporate some form of overload cut-out rated at 1 A to 2 A or, alternatively, fit an electronic cut-out such as Project 12 in *Practical Electronics for Railway Modellers*.

IC1, or T3 if a discrete transistor is used in the output stage, *must* be mounted on a substantial heat sink for, as in all closed-loop controllers, the output transistor is required to dissipate substantial power in the form of heat.

Performance

The combination of T1 and IC1 gives this circuit a current gain theoretically approaching 1,000,000. Consequently the speed regulation is excellent,

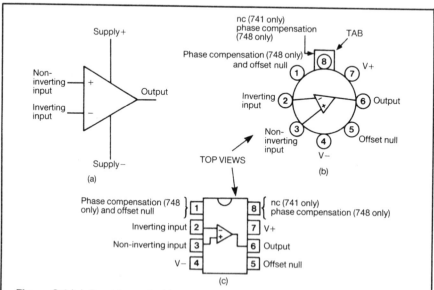

Figure 2.1 (a) Graphic symbol for an operational amplifier; **(b)** and **(c)** pin outs of the popular 741 and 748 op lamp ICs (top views); **(b)** gives the TO5 metal can version and **(c)** the 8-pin dual-in-line package.

extraordinarily so for a closed-loop controller. It produces better, smoother starts than many PWM controllers and, moreover, it does so with a silence that is eerie; the feedback system even senses lateral movement of the motor's armature and counteracts it so that locomotives which normally clatter now run silently. As a Hornby pannier tank coasts to a halt, the only sound is the drum of its wheels on the rails which is most satisfying! It is this, perhaps, as much as its low-speed performance and absolute simplicity, that has impressed many who have seen this controller in use.

Chapter 2: Ultra-high-gain closed-loop controller

The controller described in Chaper 1 owes its fine performance to two factors: (i) its very high current gain, approaching 1,000,000 and (ii) its use of an unsmoothed power supply. This suggests that further improvement might be possible by the use of an even higher current gain. This is easy to test. In the Chapter 1 circuit T1, as I pointed out, is used as a comparator, which compares the control voltage (on its base) with the controller output voltage (on its emitter). It is simple to replace T1 by an even more effective comparator — an *operational amplifier*.

Operational amplifiers

Operational amplifiers (or 'op amps') are integrated circuits very widely used in electronics. Their essential features (besides positive and negative supply terminals) are two inputs and an output terminal. The two inputs are called the *inverting input* (distinguished in circuit diagrams by a negative sign) and, rather clumsily, the *non-inverting input* (distinguished by a positive sign). (Note that the polarity of the symbols on the circuit diagram has nothing to do with the polarity of the voltage or current on these inputs — it is just a 'shorthand' way of saying that the non-inverting input must be taken positive to make the output more positive and the inverting input must be taken more negative to make the output more positive.) The graphical symbol for an op amp and the pin-outs of the 741 and 748 ICs are shown in Figure 2.1.

These two terminals provide what is known as *differential input,* that is to say, the amplifier responds to the *difference* between the potentials on the two inputs. If you interfere with the inputs, doing the same thing to *both* inputs, the amplifier ignores it, a phenomenon known as *common-mode rejection,* which makes op amps very useful in electrically noisy environments (eg adjacent to working model railways!) where such interference can cause problems. Instead, to make the output more positive, either the non-inverting input must be made more positive relative to the inverting input or the inverting input must be made more negative relative to the non-inverting input (which is another way of saying the same thing). The input resistance of op amps is very high (a few megohms) and so for practical purposes may be regarded as infinite. The voltage gain is very high. That for the archetypal op amp, the 741, which we shall be using, is quoted as typically 200,000. Thus, a differential change of only 0.1 mV on the inputs would swing the output by an incredible 20 V! This is why *op amps are never used without feedback.*

Feedback from the op amp output to one of the inputs tames the beast and

makes it useful. In fact, you could describe the action of an op amp with
feedback in the following terms: the op amp does whatever is necessary to
make the two inputs equal. Of course, the op amp cannot change both inputs,
but by changing its output it can — via the feedback — change one input and
pull it to the same level as the other.

The 741, like most op amps, has push-pull output. It can deliver up to
25 mA.

A practical controller

Simply take the controller in Chapter 1, remove T1 and replace it with a 741 as
shown in Figure 2.2. You will need a resistor in series with each input (its value
is very uncritical, but both should be the same; my prototype used 10 K). The
741 has a couple of terminals known as 'offset null' while the otherwise similar
748 has a terminal known as 'phase compensation'. These are only used in
applications demanding great precision; for general use, these terminals may
be left unconnected.

You will see that the control voltage is applied to the *inverting* input and the
feedback to the *non-inverting* input. This is because the output IC itself is an
inverting amplifier and is included in the feedback-loop. The op amp's supply-
positive and supply-negative terminals must, of course, be connected to the
supply lines of the controller. With an unsmoothed supply, the performance of
this controller is disappointing. I found this in my prototype which was noisy,
with starts and stops being rather less smooth than with the original Chapter 1
circuit but this is because op amps do not function well from unsmoothed
supplies. By adding a 2,500 μF electrolytic capacitor across the supply, (thus
making it a 23 V *smoothed* supply) a great improvement was effected and,
with an open-loop gain in the range 10^8 to 10^{10}, this combination can cope with
anything. Thus, running was silent, starts and stops were smooth while there
was a reserve of power (effectively 7 V extra) that was not present in the
Chapter 1 design.

There are, however, a number of problems in pure DC controllers like this
one. Mostly they are concerned with effects upon other equipment. This kind
of controller cannot easily be used with a speedometer (Chapter 7), nor with
live-rail track circuits (Chapters 8, 9 and 11), although it is fine with return-rail
track circuits. On the positive side this controller is suitable for use with the
accessory circuits described in Chapters 5 and 6. Probably for most modellers
the simpler circuit of Chapter 1 will be preferred. Only those who are intent
upon ultra-high speed will find this circuit advantageous.

Chapter 3: Unusual pulse-width-modulation controller

This controller is based on a design described in *Model Railway Electronics*,
No 1, February 1984. It combines simplicity with a refreshingly different
approach to pulse width modulation (PWM).

The principal advantage of PWM is the ease of control, particularly at low
speeds and when starting. The motor receives brief pulses of full power and,
because it is *full* power, there is sufficient torque to overcome friction and
inertia and to get the train rolling. Also, because the pulse soon ends, the

motor does not get the chance to go racing off as soon as it has overcome the forces that try to hold it back. A further advantage is that the output transistor, being used as a switch only, dissipates no power and therefore needs no heat sinkage. However, PWM has two principal disadvantages. One is motor heating for, in most PWM systems, a considerable proportion of the controller output is dissipated as heat in the motor windings, especially at low speeds so that even if the windings do not melt and go open circuit, the heat has a demagnetising effect. The second disadvantage is noise. The steep rise and fall of the power waveform causes the armature to rattle, so that the locos buzz angrily. With diesel-outline locos the sound can be remarkably realistic, but with steam- or electric-outline locos, it is disconcerting.

This new circuit eliminates the motor heating tendency by achieving a gentle rise in the output waveform but the cut-off is sharp, so the noise problem remains, although it is not so raucous as some PWM controllers.

How it works
At the heart of this controller is the inexpensive 555 timer IC, which we shall meet again and again in this book. It is a very useful device — in fact, whole books have been written about its applications. Some designers even use it without its timing circuit as a bistable with output stage since it has push-pull

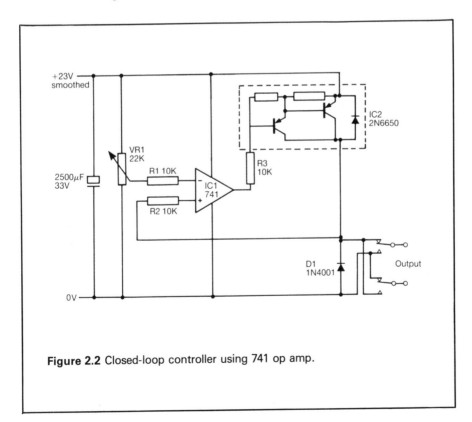

Figure 2.2 Closed-loop controller using 741 op amp.

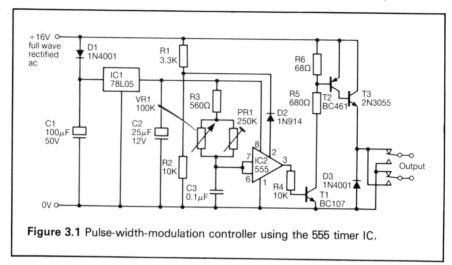

Figure 3.1 Pulse-width-modulation controller using the 555 timer IC.

output and can deliver up to 200 mA. The 555 can be used as a timer in two ways. It can be set up as a free-running multivibrator, ie an oscillator, as in Chapters 19 and 27 of this book. It can also be used as a monostable ('one-shot') which is how it is used in this Chapter (See Figure 3.1.).

When used as a one-shot, the 555 operates a cycle as follows. In its quiescent state, the output of the device (pin 3) is held *low,* ie close to the potential of the supply negative terminal. During this period the timing capacitor is held discharged by a conductive transistor in the 555 whose open collector is connected to pin 7. The one-shot starts its timing cycle when a negative-going pulse (ie a pulse at a voltage less than one third of the 555's supply) is applied to pin 2. Once triggered, the 555's output goes *high* (ie approaching its supply voltage) and the short circuit is removed from the timing capacitor, which begins to charge via the timing resistor network. When the charge on the capacitor reaches two thirds of the 555's supply voltage the device trips, the output goes low, the short circuit is applied to the timing capacitor to discharge it and the device returns to its quiescent state until another trigger pulse is applied to pin 2.

The 555 requires a smoothed power supply between 4.5 V and 18 V. In Figure 3.1 IC1 (a 78L05) is used to provide a regulated supply at 5 V, but the 78L12 IC could be used instead to provide a stabilised supply at 12 V. This variation of the operating voltage will not greatly affect the performance of the 555.

In this circuit the incoming waveform of the full-wave rectified AC supply is used to provide triggering pulses for the 555. (It is assumed that your mains supply is at 50 Hz. If it is at 60 Hz a slight adjustment will be needed.) If you operate the circuit from a half-wave rectified AC supply considerable complications will ensue.

Diode D2 provides for the 555 to be triggered whenever the power supply voltage dips below about 1.3 V. Owing to the shape of this waveform, this means virtually at the nulls which, with a 50 Hz supply, come at 10 ms (millisecond) intervals. (See Figure 3.2.)

The 555's timing network is so designed that the interval timed is adjustable roughly over the range 0.2 ms to 10 ms. At the lowest settings of the speed control, therefore, the pulses will be about 0.2 ms long but, as the speed control is advanced, the pulses will become longer until at 10 ms they merge into each other, since as one pulse ends the next will begin immediately. The 555's output is fed to the array of transistors T2/T3/T4. These, it will be noticed, are supplied from the unsmoothed, rectified AC supply and there is a good reason for this. The output stage *could* be operated from a smoothed supply, whereupon the controller would deliver a square-wave PWM output, with all the usual motor heating perils. But by operating it from the raw unsmoothed supply, with the pulses beginning at the nulls as the 555 is triggered, our controller gives a sinusoidal rise with a sharp cut-off at the end of the pulse. (This output wave form is the opposite of that obtained from controllers using thyristors; these become conductive at a stage during the cycle determined by the speed control and remain conductive until the null, when they are reset.) It is the sinusoidal rise of the output waveform that is responsible for the elimination of motor heating effects; at low speeds the motor is not subjected to the full supply voltage, as it is in square-wave PWM systems.

Resistor R3 is essential for, in conjunction with C3, it sets the minimum pulse duration. If it were zero, the minimum pulse duration would be infinitesimal since C3 would charge instantaneously, but then the transistor on the 555, whose duty it is to hold the timing capacitor discharged between cycles, would find itself connected straight across the 555's supply when the

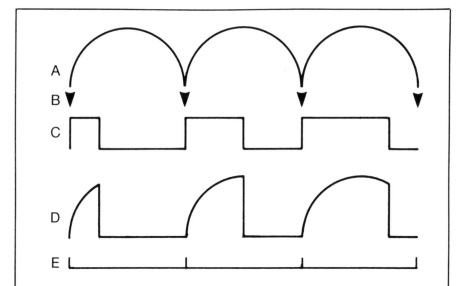

Figure 3.2 How the PWM controller's unique waveform is derived: **(a)** the incoming full-wave rectified AC waveform; **(b)** trigger pulses applied to pin 2 of the 555 at the nulls; **(c)** output of the 555 at 25, 50 and 75 per cent duty cycle respectively, representing unprototypically abrupt acceleration! **(d)** controller output, effectively the product of (a) and (c); **(e)** time scale, each division representing 10 ms (50 Hz mains assumed).

speed control is at zero. Not only would it short the 555 out, but also it would risk burn-out. So, a compromise is necessary. R3 protects the transistor but saddles one with a minimum pulse length which causes a complication in the output stage which, in turn, is resolved by the introduction of R6. The 555 is triggered whenever the power supply output, approaching the null, drops to about 1.3 V. With the speed control at a minimum the 555's output will be a pulse about 0.2 ms long, which is delivered to the output stage and therefore becomes — or attempts to become — conductive. Inevitably there is *some* supply voltage available at this time that is duly delivered to the motor which sets it buzzing and may even be sufficient to turn it. The potential divider R5/R6, however, ensures that at these low power supply voltages the T3 receives insufficient base bias to bring it into conduction. Consequently, when the speed control is at minimum, the motor is not only stationary, but silent.

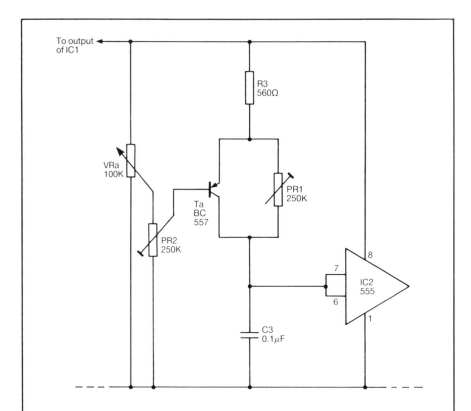

Figure 3.3 Modifications to the circuit of Figure 3.1 to make the speed control a 'straight' voltage control potentiometer. With the sliders of VRa and PR2 both set to maximum (ie, away from supply negative) set PR1 for maximum speed. Then with the slider of VRa at minimum, adjust PR2 until the train just stops. VRa should now give smooth control from minimum to maximum. Consequent upon this conversion the accessories described in Chapters 5 and 6 can be added to this controller.

Setting the controller up

Set PR1 to maximum resistance and VR1 to minimum resistance (minimum speed). With a volt meter (25 V range), motor or lamp across the output terminals of the controller, switch the controller on and advance VR1 to maximum and back a few times, watching what happens to the output. You should find that the maximum output is delivered when VR1 is roughly at its mid point. Maximum output occurs when the one-shot's timed interval equals the mains half cycle. Above this setting the output falls. Now set VR1 to maximum and back off PR1 until maximum output is obtained. You should now find that VR1 gives smooth control from minimum to maximum speed. PR1 should not need any further adjustment unless you move to a district having a different mains frequency.

Power supply requirements

As mentioned earlier, this controller circuit needs a full-wave rectified AC supply, which should be 12 V to 16 V nominal. If a half-wave rectified AC supply is used considerable modification to the timing components will be needed and a higher voltage will be needed for full speed.

The 555 must have a smoothed supply between 5 V and 18 V. The function of D1/C1/IC1 in Figure 3.1 is to provide a supply for the 555 stabilised at 5 V. Without IC1 the 555 would be subjected to a supply at about 23 V which might damage it. Needless to say, the power supply must be fitted with a current limiter or overload cut-out.

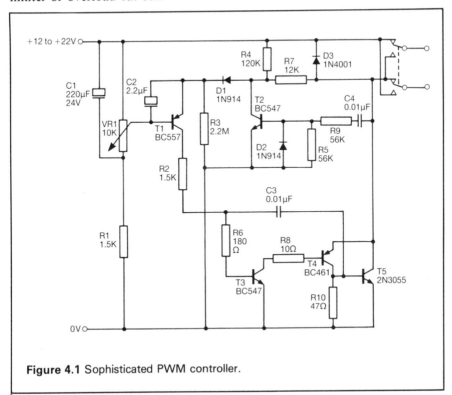

Figure 4.1 Sophisticated PWM controller.

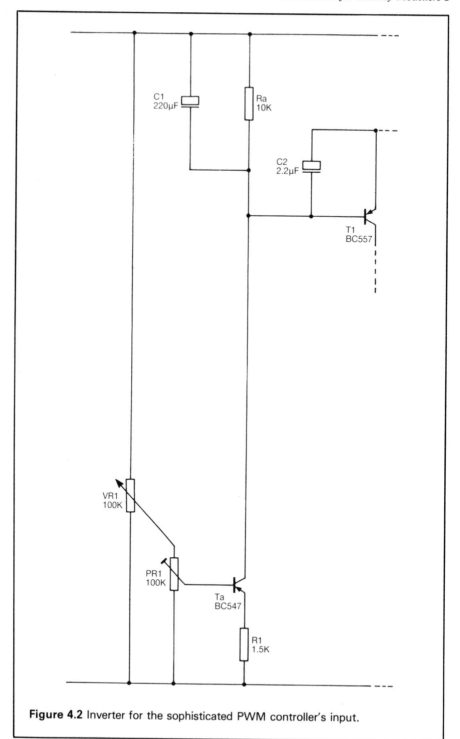

Figure 4.2 Inverter for the sophisticated PWM controller's input.

Options

This circuit is ideally suited to a number of optional extras, including use with a speedometer (Chapter 7). Figure 3.3 shows a simple modification to the timing circuit to turn the speed control into a 'straight' voltage control potentiometer. Consequent upon this modification the accessories described in Chapters 5 and 6 may be added to this controller.

Chapter 4: Sophisticated PWM controller

This controller, which gives excellent speed constancy and low-speed running, is based on a circuit designed by I.W. Rudge (*Wireless World,* September 1977, p 84). Unlike most model railway electronic projects, the circuit is quite temperamental as too much variation in the component values will cause malfunctioning. Moreover, the circuitry around T2, although seemingly a 'nicety', is essential; if it is omitted the locomotives dance jigs.

How it works

T3 and T4 form a complementary multi-vibrator which oscillates at around 100 Hz, although the frequency falls at lower settings of the speed control and, at the lowest settings when T3 is starved of bias, oscillation ceases altogether leaving both T3 and T4 'off'. Higher settings increase the bias applied to T3 lengthening the pulse widths until, at the highest settings, T3 and T4 are both permanently 'on'. Bias for the output transistor T5 is taken from the collector of T4 .

The subtlety of the circuit lies in the arrangement for the biasing of T3. While T5 is off, T1 compares the voltage set by the slider of the speed control (applied to its base) with the motor back EMF, 90 per cent of which is fed back to its emitter via the potential divider R4/R7. The circuit around T2 'kills' the pulse of inductive overshoot, produced by the loco motor when T5 switches off, which would otherwise bias T1 forwards, nullifying the good work of the back EMF monitoring. Each pulse of inductive overshoot drives T2 into conduction, reverse biasing D1 and blocking the feedback-loop. The motor back EMF is proportional to its speed, so the effect of the feedback-loop in this circuit is to 'lock' the motor at the speed set by the speed control.

Power supply

This controller can be operated from unsmoothed or smoothed supplies, making it ideal for use if you should ever wish to run your model railway from batteries. Recommended operating voltages are 12 V to 16 V (smoothed) or 16 V to 22 V (unsmoothed).

Practical considerations

The only real disadvantage of this circuit is that is uses a positive-earth configuration. For instance, if you wish to add on the inertia simulator shown in Figure 13.1 of *Practical Electronics for Railway Modellers,* you would have to invert it. This is not too difficult, however, since that particular circuit shows complementary symmetry. All that is necessary is to swap the functions of the inertia and brake controls but, if you wished to add on the circuits described in Chapters 5 or 6 in this book, you would have some real work to do. Alternatively, you could add the inverter, shown in Figure 4.2, on to the front end of the controller first and then any of the add-on units mentioned earlier could be installed without further modification. Pre-set resistor PR1 should be adjusted so that the speed control just covers the full speed range.

You could probably get away without using a heat sink on the output transistor, but it is probably wise to fit a small one.

Part 2

Accessories for controllers

Introduction

This section of the book describes three accessory units that may be added to electronic controllers individually or in any combination. These are a bidirectional converter, which makes one-knob control of both speed and direction possible, an 'autostop' unit that can be used manually or electronically to provide automatic gentle stops and starts and, lastly, a speedometer. None of these units affect the *performance* of the controller to which it is connected in any way but each makes operation of the controller more interesting and challenges the model train operator to perfect the same skills that are demanded of the driver of the prototype!

An Appendix after Chapter 7 gives the complete circuit diagram and parts list for a high-quality, full-feature controller combining the closed-loop control unit of Chapter 1 with all three accessories described in Chapters 5 to 7.

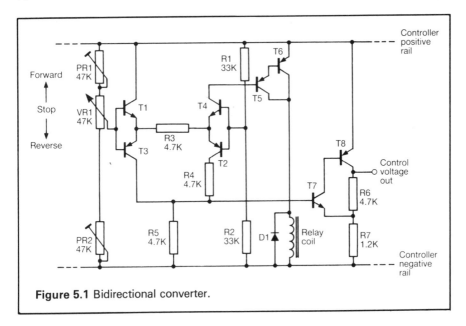

Figure 5.1 Bidirectional converter.

Chapter 5: Bidirectional converter unit

Do you remember those rheostat controllers in which there was a single combined speed and direction control? There was a central 'stop' position; turning the knob to the left controlled speed in one direction and turning it to the right of 'stop' controlled speed in the other direction. It certainly made operation very easy and eliminated the troubles that can be caused by faulty direction-change switches. This type of rheostat controller is still available from some suppliers, as is at least one kind of electronic controller with a similar control arrangement. It is possible, however, to add on a converter unit to many types of conventional electronic controller to give this same kind of 'one-knob' control. Figure 5.1 shows one possible converter circuit.

How it works

Transistors T1/T2/T3/T4 form a bridge circuit. Since resistors R1/R2 have the same value, the voltage on the bases of T2/T4 equals half the supply voltage and the voltage on their emitters is held at about the same voltage. When speed/direction control VR1 is at its mid-point setting, the voltage on its slider is again equal to half the supply voltage. Consequently no bias is applied to any of the bridge transistors, no current flows through bridge resistor R3 and no control voltage appears across R5. Thus the train is stopped. Now, let us move the slider of the speed control towards the positive rail; we shall call this the *forwards* direction. The base voltage applied to T1/T3 rises, bringing T1 and (via R3) T2 into conduction. The conduction path is T1/R3/T2/R4/R5. As the speed control is advanced the current flowing through R5 raises a voltage across it which rises to about one fifth of the supply voltage when the speed control reaches maximum. If the speed control is now returned through the central 'stop' position and on into the 'reverse' zone, so that the slider is now nearer to the negative rail than to the positive, T3 and T4 are brought into conduction instead of T1/T2. The conduction path is now T6/T5 (base/emitter junctions) T4/R3/T3/R5.

There is a reason for the inclusion of R4 in the collector circuit of T2. The bridge is not symmetrical. If R4 were omitted, the collector of T2 now being connected directly to R5 and the collector of T3, the maximum voltage obtainable across R5 (from which the speed control voltage for the controller itself is derived) would vary according to the direction selected. This is because the voltage applied to the base of T3 can vary over a wide range, whereas that on the base of T2 is held at half the supply voltage. Consequently, when reversing, the voltage on the base of T3 falls as that on its collector rises, the limit being when these are equal at about one quarter of the supply voltage. When running forwards, however, the base of T2 is held at half the supply voltage and the voltage across R5 (in the absence of R4) could rise almost to this voltage. Resistor R4 'swallows' some of this giving a more even range of control voltages across R5. So, turning the slider to either extreme raises voltage of constant polarity across R5, from which is derived a control voltage for the controller, but only in the *lower* half of the slider's travel is bias supplied to Darlington pair T5/T6. This has as its collector load the coil of a relay having (at least) double-pole, double-throw (DPDT) contacts which replace the direction-change switch contacts. Thus, the train's direction is changed over half of the control range. Diode D1 kills inductive overshoot

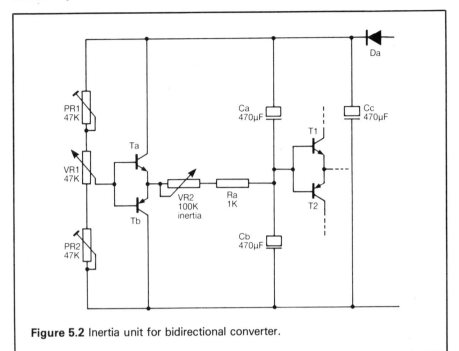

Figure 5.2 Inertia unit for bidirectional converter.

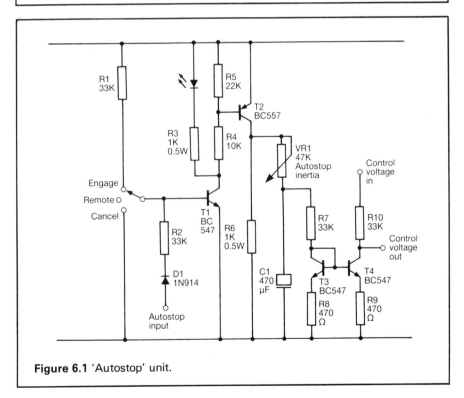

Figure 6.1 'Autostop' unit.

when the relay coil is de-energised. However, because the maximum voltage obtained across R5 is only about one fifth (perhaps a little more) of the supply voltage, this must be restored to full range before being fed to the controller. This is the function of *quasi*-Darlington pair T7/T8. Resistors R6/R7 are chosen so that R6 equals four times R7. The output voltage is taken from across both resistors and this arrangement feeds back one fifth of the output voltage to T7. That is to say, this circuit's output voltage equals five times its input voltage.

Use of this unit

The circuit as described may be used with any electronic controller requiring a *positive-going* input voltage, such as those in Chapters 1 or 2 of this book and in Chapter 4, if the optional inverter is included. It may also be used with Projects 6, 7, 9 or 10 in *Practical Electronics for Railway Modellers*. It shares the controller's power supply, whether smoothed or unsmoothed. Pre-set resistors PR1 and PR2 should be adjusted so that full speed is just reached at the limits of travel of VR1's slider.

If you have a controller requiring a *negative-going* control voltage, eg Chapter 4 in this book *without* the optional inverter, you will need to construct a complementary version of the unit.

Inertia unit

An inertia unit may be added to the bidirectional converter unit. Its circuit is shown in Figure 5.2. With the component values shown, the response time to changes of the speed control setting is variable over the range 0.5 to about 50 seconds. Shunting at high settings of the inertia control is great fun! A rapid flip from, say, moderate forwards to moderate reverse gives a gradual deceleration to a standstill followed by a gradual restart in the opposite direction, which is very realistic to watch. It is also a real test of the 'driver's' skill judging the braking distances. Exactly as on the prototype!

The inertia circuit *must* have a smoothed power supply. If the rest of the controller has an unsmoothed power supply, incorporate D1 and C3 as shown. Otherwise, they may be omitted.

Chapter 6: 'Autostop' unit for automatic gentle stops and starts

It is very easy to arrange for trains to stop dead and suddenly restart. All that is necessary is to interrupt the electrical feed to the section of track on which the train is running. Several manufacturers sell what they call 'automatic signal kits' in which the switch that sets the signal to danger also isolates a short stretch of track on the approach and clearing the signal restores the power. So, the train approaching the danger signal stops dead very unprototypically and restarts, with equally unprototypical abruptness, when the signal clears.

The only way to achieve fully-controlled automatic stops and starts is to gradually reduce the control voltage to zero at the input of an electronic controller and then to gradually restore it to its former level. That is the function of the 'autostop' units described in this Chapter. The comprehensive unit whose circuit is given in Figure 6.1 was developed for use in conjunction with the interlock system described in Chapter 23, but has many other possible applications, eg timed station stops (Chapter 24).

An input terminal is provided for remote controlled operation, but the unit can also be operated manually. A three-position switch, which may be a single-pole double-throw switch having a centre 'off' position, controls its functions. When this switch is put in the 'engage' position, the train will gently decelerate and stop. When the switch is put in the central 'remote' position, the train will stop if a positive-going voltage is applied to the remote input terminal; otherwise it will continue to run or, if previously stopped using the 'engage' mode, it will gently restart and accelerate to the speed set by the controller. When the switch is put in the 'cancel' position, the train will run normally or will restart gradually if previously stopped by the unit, even if a positive-going voltage is still being applied to the remote input. The rate of slow-down and acceleration is determined by a special inertia control quite independent of any already fitted to the controller.

How it works

A positive-going voltage on the base of T1 drives it into conduction, lighting the optional 'autostop' indicator LED 1. It also biases T2 into conduction, whereupon nearly the whole of the supply voltage appears across R6. Inertia capacitor C1 now begins to charge, the rate of charge being determined by inertia control VR1. As this capacitor charges, the current being fed via R7 into T3 increases proportionately. Now T3 and T4 form what is called a 'current mirror'. This is a circuit in which the current fed into the collector of one transistor (T3 in this circuit) causes an equal current to flow in the collector circuit of another transistor (T4). For a current mirror to work properly the two transistors must be an accurately matched pair.

In a transistor the collector current is, in fact, controlled by the *voltage* applied across the base/emitter junction but, because a very wide range of collector current is controlled by a very tightly confined sweep of bias voltage (around 0.7 V for a silicon transistor), it is, as a rule, not practical to regard a transistor as a voltage-controlled device. This circuit is the exception to that rule. In a current mirror the input current is applied to both collector and base of the first transistor. This has the effect of making that transistor automatically adjust its base/emitter voltage so that the collector current *just* sinks the available input current, less the negligible base bias current. Now, if we connect the base/emitter junction of a second *identical* transistor in parallel with that of the first transistor, since it receives the same input voltage as the first, it will sink the same collector current. That is to say, output current equals input current. In this application, the second transistor of the current mirror, together with its collector load resistor (R10), forms a potential divider. The control voltage from the controller's speed control or speed/inertia circuit is applied to the 'top' of R10 and the output is taken from the collector of the transistor. The effect of this is that the circuit attenuates (ie reduces) the control voltage by an amount proportional to the charge on C1. So, as C1 charges, the control voltage gradually falls until it is so close to zero that the train stops.

When the positive voltage is removed from the base of T1, this transistor ceases to conduct, as does T2. Capacitor C1 now discharges via VR1 and R6; R6 is negligible compared to most settings of VR1 and so generally has little

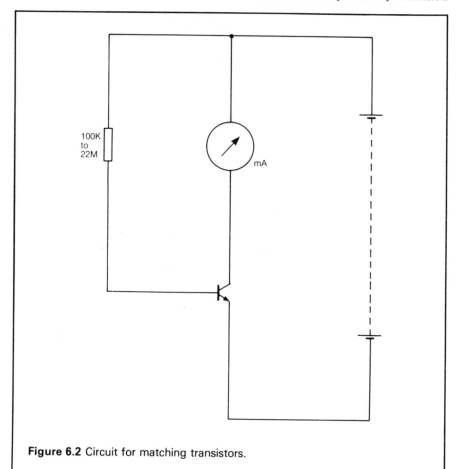

Figure 6.2 Circuit for matching transistors.

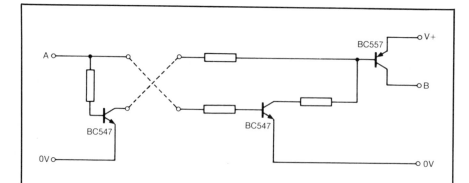

Figure 6.3 Interface unit for linking two circuits having different 'ground' potentials. A positive-going input at A gives a positive-going output at B despite potential differences between the two 0 V rails. All resistors 33K.

effect on the delay. As C1 discharges, the current flowing into T3 gradually falls and so does the collector current of T4. Consequently the control voltage applied to the input of the controller gradually rises and the train restarts and accelerates gently away.

Practical considerations

The unit as described is suitable only for controllers needing a positive-going input voltage, eg those in Chapters 1 and 2 in this book and also Chapter 4, if the optional inverter is fitted. It is also suitable for Projects 6, 7, 9 and 10 in *Practical Electronics for Railway Modellers*. If you have a controller with a negative-going input voltage, eg as in Chapter 4 of this book *without* the inverter, you will need to construct a complementary version of this unit, (eg npn for pnp transistors and *vice versa* as well as all polarised components reversed).

This unit must have a *smoothed* power supply. If this is not available, add a 1N4001 rectifier diode between the unit's positive rail and the unsmoothed supply's positive terminal and add a 1000 μF 24 V electrolytic capacitor across the unit's supply rails. You will need to match a pair of transistors for T3 and T4. Test the gains of a selection of individuals of the same type using the circuit shown in Figure 6.2. For various values of bias resistor between 100 K and 22 M choose the two transistors that give the closest values of collector current. The inclusion of R8 and R9 in the emitter circuits of T3 and T4 will compensate for minor mismatching.

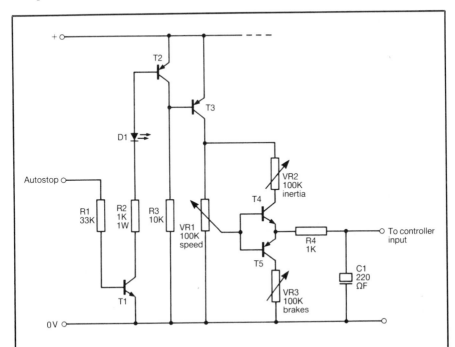

Figure 6.4 A 'low cost' alternative 'autostop' system using the regular inertia and brake controls.

This unit, as mentioned earlier, was originally intended for use in conjunction with the active interlock systems described in Chapter 23 of this book. Now, those circuits operate from the same power supply as the track circuit/signalling system, whereas this unit operates from the same power supply as the controller to which it is an appendage. Because of the controller's reversible output the 'ground' rails of the controller and the signalling system may be at different potentials. If the controller has a positive-going output (before the reversing switch) you should find that a single-wire connection from the interlock output to the 'autostop' remote input socket works satisfactorily, but otherwise a relay, an opto-isolator, or the interface unit shown in Figure 6.3, should be used to maintain the potential difference between the two circuits.

A further application for this unit is in computerised control. A logical '1' from a computer output port applied to the remote input will stop the train. With a medium to high setting of the autostop inertia and a high setting of the speed control, a PWM computer output applied to the input can even be used to control speed, as well as stopping and starting.

Alternative 'autostop' unit

The unit described is, in many ways, a 'de luxe' unit suitable for fitting to almost any controller and which can be used in conjunction with the bidirectional control system described in Chapter 5. Moreover, it has its own inertia or delay control quite independent of any inertia control that may be fitted to the 'main' controller.

Figure 6.4 shows how an 'autostop' facility can be fitted to a traditional inertia/brake voltage control circuit. With this arrangement 'autostop' does not have its own inertia control but shares the 'main' inertia and brake controls and, if these are set low, the 'autostop' will give sudden starts and stops. This unit is, however, fairly simple and inexpensive. In electronics, as in so many areas of life, 'you gets what you pays for'.

Chapter 7: Speedometer

A speedometer on a controller can give a lot of added interest to model railway operation. For instance, speed limits can be assigned to stretches of line and the operator must then use his skill to keep the train on schedule but within the speed limits! Adding a current meter in series with the output will not, however, give an indication of speed. Current consumed, for instance, will *rise* when the train climbs a gradient, when its speed is liable to *fall*. Similarly, a voltmeter across the controller output, although it gives a more accurate indication of speed than the current meter, will indicate controller output voltage rather than train speed. For example, it will read the controller output voltage even when there is no train on the track.

The only way to obtain a tolerably accurate indication of the train speed is to add a voltmeter circuit across the output of the controller *and to strobe it* so that it only functions during those brief occasions when the controller output transistor is *not* conducting. (Remember that most controllers deliver pulses of output, either by virtue of PWM or of an unsmoothed power supply.) In this way, what the meter indicates is the motor back EMF, which is proportional train speed. A practical problem is that the sampling time in a PWM controller

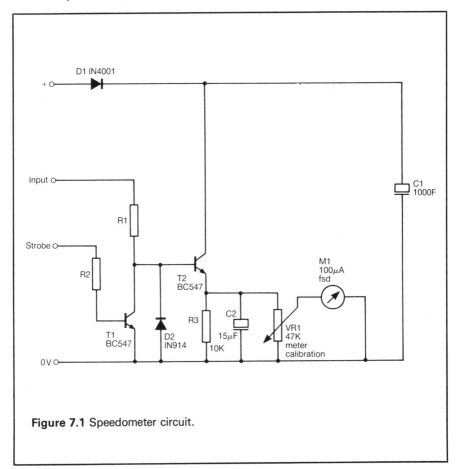

Figure 7.1 Speedometer circuit.

is brief and becomes briefer as the speed control is advanced. So, the speedometer circuit must be a 'sample and hold' circuit in which a capacitor is charged up during the samples and holds its charge until replenished by the next sample. In certain PWM controllers there is an insurmountable difficulty; at a certain high setting of the speed control the pulses merge into a continuous full power output and this disables the speedometer circuit so that it registers zero. Another difficulty is that the speedometer needs separate calibration for each locomotive in use, but more of this later. Figure 7.1 shows the practical circuit diagram of a speedometer for a controller with positive-going output before the reversing switch. A complementary version will be needed for controllers, such as the one in Chapter 4, which have negative-going output before the reversing switch.

How it works
The voltage at the output of a controller consists of three components when in normal use. During the power pulses there is the voltage that the controller itself is delivering. At the end of each pulse there is a spike of inductive over-shoot from the locomotive motor, which, as measured by a voltmeter across

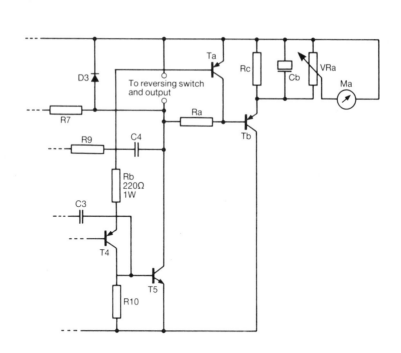

Figure 7.2 How to adapt the speedometer circuit for use with the PWM controller described in Chapter 4 which has positive earth and a smoothed supply. Numbered components are as in Figure 4.1. Components from Figure 7.1 have the letters a, b, c in place of the numbers 1, 2 3.

the output terminals, is of opposite polarity to the controller output. Lastly, also only distinguishable between power pulses, is the motor back EMF. This, as measured by a voltmeter across the output terminals, is of the same polarity as the controller output and, because it is proportional to motor speed, it is this which we wish to isolate and indicate on our speedometer.

The speedometer circuit input is taken from the controller output (before the reversing switch) and applied via resistor R1 to the base of T2. The strobe input is applied via current-limiting resistor R2 to the base of T1 which forms the lower limb of a potential divider with R1. The effect of this is that T2 only receives an input during the spaces between power pulses; during the pulses themselves T2's input is short-circuited away by T1. Diode D2 is to kill inductive overshoot although it may be omitted if there is already an overshoot-killing diode across the controller output, as in Chapters 1 to 4.

Transistor T2 is used as an emitter follower and even brief pulses of input cause it to charge C2 up to the input voltage (less the offset of about 0.7 V). Resistor R3 allows C2 to discharge at a moderate rate; the values of C2 and R3 should be chosen to give a time constant of 0.15 seconds, equalling about 15 pulses, with recommended values of 10 μF and 15 K. Thus, a voltage is maintained across C2/R3 which is tolerably proportional to train speed. It is recommended that the meter be a 100 μA type for which there are two reasons. Firstly, it enables the selection of a high value of calibration potentiometer, eg 47 K, which will have a minimal effect on the functioning of the circuit and secondly, it is easy to pretend that the units of calibration are not μA, but scale mph, with 100 mph as the full-scale reading.

Installation

The installation of this unit depends on the kind of controller to which it is being connected. If the controller is a closed-loop type, eg as in Chapter 1, both the strobe input and positive connection, shown in Figure 7.1, should be connected to the controller's positive rail. If the controller is a PWM type the strobe input should be connected to some point in the controller which goes positive in synchronisation with the output pulses, but not the controller output itself (because of interference from other positive sources there, such as the back EMF that we are trying to measure). Some modification to the controller circuit may be needed in order to provide a suitable strobe input. Figure 7.2 shows part of the circuit from Chapter 4 suitably modified to provide a strobe input for the speedometer (taken from the emitter of T4), but note that the speedometer circuit is a complementary type, since this controller has a negative-going output.

If the controller has a *smoothed* power supply D1 and C1 may be omitted. This has been assumed in Figure 7.2, although Chapter 4's circuit may be operated from smoothed or unsmoothed supplies.

Calibration

Set a train running at a guessed scale speed of 50 mph. Now, adjust VR1 until the meter reads 50 (half scale) and try varying the train speed. You should find that the meter reading is indeed proportional to the train speed. Moreover, if you lift the train off the track while it is still running, the speedometer should drop to zero, or nearly so. For more accurate calibration, you will need a stop watch and a measured length of track, say 1 yard (0.91 m), over which to measure train time. The Table below shows how the time taken in seconds to cover 1 yard relates to scale speed for some popular model railway scales.

Scale	Scale speed in mph (km/h)							
(mm/ft)	10 (16)	20 (32)	30 (48)	40 (64)	50 (80)	60 (96)	70 (112)	80 (128)
2.00 (N)	31	16	10	7.8	6.2	5.2	4.4	3.9
3.50 (HO)	18	8.8	5.9	4.4	3.6	3.0	2.5	2.2
4.00 (OO/EM)	16	7.8	5.2	3.9	3.1	2.6	2.2	1.9
7.00 (O)	8.9	4.4	3.0	2.2	1.8	1.5	1.3	1.1

VR1 should be calibrated, eg 1 to 10, and each locomotive in use tested, referring to the Table, and the correct setting of VR1 recorded for it. Calibration varies from loco to loco because it is dependent upon such variables as gearing, driving wheel size and motor characteristics. Keep a list of your locos with the appropriate VR1 setting for each by your controller.

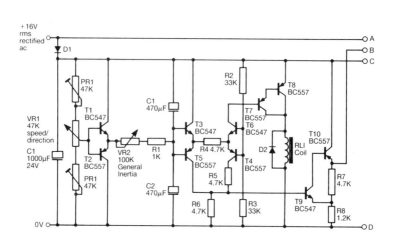

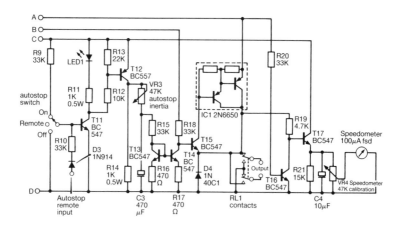

Figure A1.1 Complete circuit diagram of a full feature controller combining circuits from Chapters 1, 5 (with inertia), 6 and 7.

Use with other electronic systems

The speedometer circuit described may be used on layouts fitted with track circuits (see Part 3), but a few words of warning are in order. Provided that the loco is making good contact with the track, the track circuit voltage will be short-circuited harmlessly away so cannot interfere with the speedometer reading. However, if the loco fails to make proper contact with the track, the track circuit voltage will be applied across the speedometer input. In practice, when a loco is making only intermittent contact with the track, each interruption leads to a momentary peak of speed reading or a momentary zero reading, depending on the setting of the controller's direction switch. If there is no loco in any section connected to the controller the speedometer will, of course, register a permanent high speed or a permanent zero, depending again on the setting of the direction switch.

The use of a high-frequency coach lighting system (Chapter 27) will cause spurious readings on the speedometer but this cannot be avoided. I have made many experiments with capacitors inserted all over the speedometer circuit to find an arrangement that filters out the high-frequency AC, but although it is easy to kill the high-frequency the desirable back EMF always vanishes as well! The same applies to through-the-rails sound (Chapter 30).

Appendix 1: Putting it all together

Chapters 5 to 7 describe a number of accessory units, all of which may be added to the same controller, eg that described in Chapter 1. But how do you put them all together?

Primarily for the benefit of those readers without much experience of electronics and who may be unsure about the various connections that are needed is Figure A1.1 which shows the complete circuit diagram of a full-feature control unit consisting of the closed-loop controller described in Chapter 1, plus all three accessory units from Chapters 5, 6 and 7. The bidirectional converter (Chapter 5) includes the optional inertia simulator. If the complete circuit appears daunting, just divide it into its component parts. Up to T10 it is Chapter 5; from T11 to T14 it is Chapter 6; around T15 and IC1 it is Chapter 1 while around T16 and T17 it is Chapter 7. So, if you wish to build this complete unit I recommend that you do it by stages. Build the circuit in Chapter 1 first and test it thoroughly before adding any of the accessories. Then add the 'autostop' unit, taking the 'top' end of R18 to the slider of the speed control potentiometer. Test this thoroughly before you put in the bidirectional converter unit *without* inertia. (This means that the bases of T3/T5 go temporarily direct to the slider of VR1.) If this works satisfactorily add the inertia-simulator components, T1/T2/VR2 and R1. The speedometer unit can be added at any stage.

Parts needed
Semiconductors: 10 × BC547, or similar small-signal npn transistor.
                            7 × BC557, or similar small-signal pnp transistor.
                            3 × 1N4001 rectifier diode.
                            1 × 2N6650 power pnp Darlington IC.

Resistors:	2 × 470Ω
	3 × 1 K ½ W
	1 × 1.2 K
	5 × 4.7 K
	1 × 10 K
	1 × 15 K
	1 × 22 K
	7 × 33 K
Capacitors:	3 × 470 μF 24 V wkg
	1 × 10 μF 24 V wkg
Potentiometers:	3 × 47 K (or 50 K) linear
	1 × 100 K linear
	2 × 47 K pre-set
Miscellaneous:	1 LED
	1 × 100 μA meter
	1 relay (12 V coil, DPDT (at least) contacts.)
	1 DPDT switch with centre-off position.

Part 3

Track Circuiting

Introduction

Only one system of train detection is considered in detail in this book — *track circuiting*. By this I mean only those systems of train detection which work — as on the prototype — by monitoring the electrical continuity of a section of line. Some railway modellers also use the term *track circuiting* loosely and, in my opinion incorrectly, to describe other train detection systems, especially magnet/reed switch/bistable-based systems, which may be set up to imitate track circuiting by indicating the presence of trains in sections or blocks. I have deliberately confined this section of the book to track circuiting in the narrow sense because it is, in my opinion, the simplest, the most versatile, the most reliable and, not least, the most prototypical method of train detection. Its advantages so outweigh those of other train detection systems that these are not worthy of serious consideration except on certain existing layouts where the provision of rail breaks essential for track circuiting may be precluded by problems of access. For alternative systems of train detection see *Practical Electronics for Railway Modellers,* Projects 15 and 16 as well as Chapter 12 in this book.

Track circuiting demands no modification whatever to locomotives and the only modification to the track is its division into track-circuited sections by means of rail breaks or insulating fishplates. These may be in one rail or both, depending on track circuit type. Each track-circuited section must, of necessity, have its own feed from the controller(s) and the track circuit unit is wired into this feed. Sections may be long, eg blocks for signalling purposes, or short, eg for accessory operation, the lower limit being the electrical wheelbase of the longest locomotive (or other conductive vehicle) in use, since the section must be long enough to ensure that the locomotive (or other vehicle) draws current in it. Either rail, or even both, may be track-circuited. There are, however, subtle differences between live-rail and return-rail track circuits, which must be taken into account in layout planning.

Track circuit units need not be complicated. Chapter 8 introduces a unidirectional live-rail unit using ony two transistors and a handful of other components. Chapter 10 describes a return-rail version, which is only slightly more complex. Unidirectional track circuits, as their name suggests, normally permit the movement of trains in one direction only. Quite simple arrangements can be made, however, to permit reversing when needed. *Quasi-bidirectional* track circuits are unidirectional circuits equipped with automatic electronic switching to permit reversing. Chapter 9 describes a quasi-bidirectional live-rail track circuit.

Chapter 11 is concerned with fully bidirectional track circuits and after outlining the principles underlying the celebrated 'twin-T' track circuit and its derivatives, my own EDOTIS (described more fully in *Practical Electronics for Railway Modellers*) is introduced as an example of a *return-rail* bidirectional track circuit. (In *Practical Electronics for Railway Modellers* it was used somewhat disadvantageously as a live-rail unit; the complications disappear when it is used in the return-rail mode.) Finally, a modified EDOTIS, called EDOTIS II, is described, which is a fully bidirectional, live-rail, common-return track circuit of some sophistication. All the track circuits described in this book share the layout common return. Consequently, any number of units, of the same type or of mixed types, on the same layout may share the same power supply irrespective of the number of controllers in use.

Output and other considerations

Before embarking on any track circuiting project, a number of matters must be settled. Obviously, you must decide which rail is to be monitored and whether you need a unidirectional or bidirectional unit. These matters will be determined largely by the geography of your layout and by the kind of operations that you expect to take place in the sections which you are track circuiting. Ideally you should read through Parts 3, 4 and 5 of this book and then choose the track circuit type that is most appropriate to your needs. However, one other variable must be settled before you get out your soldering iron and that is the output facility required, which again will depend on the application that you have in mind for your track circuits.

Recently, amidst the largely uncharted sea of model railway electronics a convention has emerged regarding track circuit (and other train detection system) outputs. This convention states that a unit generally has one output only and this gives a TTL-compatible logical '0' when a train is detected. (For an explanation of these terms see Appendix 4.) This convention arises from the increasing use of TTL (transistor/transistor logic) in signalling circuits and automatic train control circuits. The easiest way to provide such an output is to take the track circuit output from the collector of an npn transistor, whose emitter is grounded and which is biased into saturation when a train is detected. The TTL system being driven will, of course, share the track circuit common return, although not necessarily its power supply. It is desirable, but

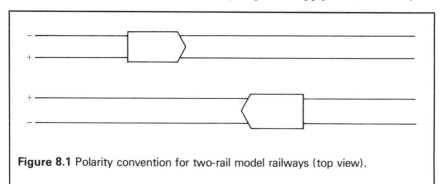

Figure 8.1 Polarity convention for two-rail model railways (top view).

not essential, to connect a pull-up resistor (1 K to 10 K) between the collector and the TTL positive supply. This 'pulls up' the TTL input to supply positive potential when the transistor is 'off'. You can kill two birds with one stone by making this resistor lower (180 Ω to 560 Ω) and putting in series with it an LED as a 'section occupied' indicator. All but one of the track circuits described in this book have this kind of single output. All of the signalling systems described in Part 4 (which use TTL throughout) assume this same kind of track circuit output, as do those circuits in Part 5 which require input from a track circuit. The one exception is EDOTIS, which was purpose-designed for driving two-aspect signals using grain-of-wheat bulbs and, as described, has an antiphase pair of positive-going outputs which deliver the full track circuit supply voltage. These outputs are *not* TTL-compatible. If you wish to use EDOTIS with TTL, you must modify the circuit (given in Figure 11.2) from T3 onwards as shown in Figure 11.3.

The availability of versatile and reliable track circuits will, I am convinced, lead to greater advances in model railway operation than even 'command control' systems have done. The time is coming when every layout of exhibition standard will be track circuited throughout — some already are. The track circuits may operate an automatic signalling system, but, perhaps more importantly, will light LED displays in a mimic diagram of the layout so that concealed operators will know exactly where trains are and, possibly with even greater significance, the track circuits may provide the essential inputs to a progressive cab control system (Chapter 26) in which individual controllers are automatically switched from section to section as the trains move around the layout.

Chapter 8: Live-rail unidirectional track circuit

The principles underlying this, the simplest of two-rail track circuits, were formulated by Paul Mallery in 1947, when he described what is now known as the NMRA track circuit which uses relays. This is a transistorised version of his circuit. It is said to be *unidirectional* because in normal use trains can run in only one direction when in track-circuited sections. Simple arrangements can be made, however, to permit reversing which will be described later. The first requirement is to divide the layout into separate track-circuited sections by means of rail breaks. These may be in one rail only or, if one system of reversing is used (see later), in both rails.

Polarity

The division of the layout into sections entails the adoption of two conventions regarding polarity. The first relates to the polarity of the electrification of two-rail model railways. Imagine that your head is positioned over a line and you are looking up the line, seeing the rails recede into the distance. Now imagine that there is a train running on the line. If the train is moving away from you, the rail on the *right* is *positive* and if the train is coming towards you, the line on the *left* is positive. This is summarised in Figure 8.1. The second polarity convention is one widely adopted in electronics as a consequence of the chemistry of silicon from which most semiconductor devices are made. This makes the 'earth' or 'ground', or common-return line of an electric circuit the most *negative* part of the circuit, ie this line is connected to the negative

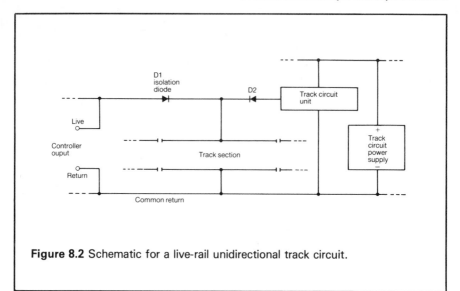

Figure 8.2 Schematic for a live-rail unidirectional track circuit.

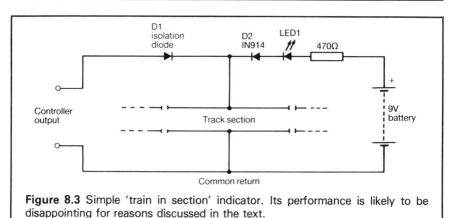

Figure 8.3 Simple 'train in section' indicator. Its performance is likely to be disappointing for reasons discussed in the text.

terminal of the power supply. This type of track circuit is sometimes called a 'shunt' track circuit (no connection with railway shunting) because the track circuit is connected across the track (it *shunts* it in the electrical sense) while most other track circuits are *series* types. To prevent the controller output from interfering unduly with the track circuit's operation, a heavy-duty diode is included in the live feed from the controller to the isolated track section. Figure 8.2 shows how this diode effectively isolates the controller from the track circuit; electrically they cannot 'see' each other. In practice D2 in the Figure may not exist as a discrete component, it is simply drawn to indicate that the track circuit unit only responds to negative-going inputs. Diode D1 is known as the *isolation diode* and it also serves to isolate the track circuit from any other track circuits or track sections connected to the same controller. To get from one section to another would involve passing through two isolation diodes in series, anode to anode which, clearly, is impossible.

Now we can see why it is that polarity plays such an important part in the design of this kind of track circuit. For the system to work, the controller output (for normal forwards movement) and the track circuit power supply must have the *same* polarity relative to a common return. From the electronics convention, negative equals common return, so controller output 'live' is positive. So, in Chapters 8 to 10, which are concerned with unidirectional track circuits, the live rail is always assumed to be positive for normal forward running. Thus, we can decide which rail is live and which is return for any section in the layout. If the section is isolated in one rail only, it is the *live* rail that must be isolated. The return rail may be continuous, but if there is a reverse loop or a triangular junction in the layout, a reversible section isolated in both rails will be needed.

How it works

When a train arrives in the track-circuited section it completes not one but *two* separate circuits — one through the isolating diode to the controller and the other through the 'shunt' track circuit. The track circuit could be very simple indeed. For instance, if we only wanted a visual indication that the track section was occupied, all we need do (at first thought) is to add an LED with a series resistor and a power supply, which could be simply a 9 V battery. We should also need a series diode to prevent the LED from being reverse biased when the controller output exceeds the track circuit supply voltage, as is likely on occasions. The resulting simple track circuit is shown in Figure 8.3. Yet, if you try this circuit you will probably find its performance disappointing. The LED lights brightly enough when the train is stationary or moving slowly, but when it is at speed the LED will be dim and may even be extinguished altogether. This is because at speed a high voltage is raised across the locomotive motor and this opposes the LED's supply voltage, limiting the current that it can draw and perhaps even reverse biasing the series diode, so that no current can flow at all. This problem could be solved quite easily by using a track circuit supply voltage higher than any voltage that the controller is likely to deliver, eg 25 V, but it is far more convenient to use a 9 V or 12 V supply, since these are easier to obtain and offer the convenience of running grain-of-wheat bulbs as signal aspects direct from the track circuit outputs. There is, however, a way to obtain a more consistently accurate output from a unidirectional track circuit, even when operating from supplies at 9 V or less. We replace the LED with the input circuit of a pnp Darlington pair, giving the practical circuit diagram shown in Figure 8.4.

Capacitor C2 is useful for, as has already been seen, when a train is at speed peaks of voltage across the track may exceed the track circuit voltage. As with the LED under these conditions the Darlington will cease conducting. Without the capacitor the LED would be extinguished momentarily and successions of these extinctions would cause it to appear dim. The capacitor acts as a reservoir being topped up whenever the Darlington conducts and discharging through the LED whenever the Darlington ceases to conduct. Thus it keeps the LED at full brightness. It follows that if you use a controller that delivers steady DC, this type of track circuit will not work. With this type of controller a return-rail track circuit is almost essential, but see Chapter 30. This also helps considerably when the track circuit is used as part of a signalling system. It is important that, when the section is occupied, the track circuit output be

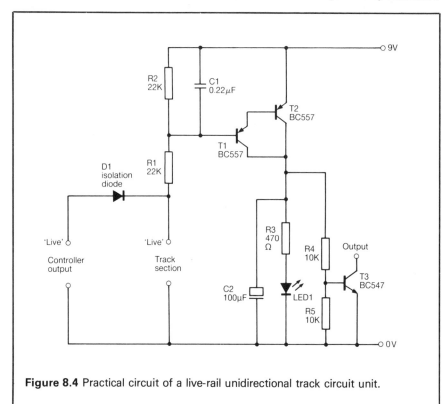

Figure 8.4 Practical circuit of a live-rail unidirectional track circuit unit.

continuous. Any interruption of its ouput, however brief, may be interpreted as 'section vacant' and may cause a green or yellow aspect to light intermittently. So, repeated interruptions would cause signal aspects to alternate rapidly (to the confusion of the train driver!). The smoothing capacitor eliminates this difficulty.

With BC557s or similar, up to 200 mA may be drawn from the track circuit's output terminal while the section is occupied. This may be used to light the red aspect of a signal, or it may provide an input for another electronic unit of some kind or it may energise a relay coil if needed. A second output terminal, antiphase with the first, may also be provided for driving a green aspect. This requires additional circuitry which may be copied from the EDOTIS bidirectional units described in Chapter 11.

Reversing

There is a price to pay for the simplicity of this kind of track circuit. This is the effect of the all-important isolation diode, for, since it blocks reverse current from the controller, trains cannot be reversed unless special arrangements are made.

There are two ways in which a reversing facility may be provided. If the section is isolated in *both* rails a two-pole, two-way reversing switch may be introduced between the track circuit unit and the two rails of the section. To reverse, throw this switch and set the controller for *forwards* movement. The train will reverse and the track circuit will continue to function normally but care must be taken if the train reaches the end of the section, for, unless the next section is also set for reverse polarity, a short circuit may be caused if a metal-tyred wheel bridges the gap between the two sections. If the section is isolated in one rail only, a simpler alternative is to add a switch to short-circuit the isolating diode. It is recommended that this switch be a non-locking push-button type with normally-open contacts. To reverse, hold the button down and set the controller to reverse. The train will reverse normally as long as the button is pressed and there will be no polarity problems when it reaches the next section. However, while the button is pressed the isolation from adjacent sections is lost and the track circuit will not function normally. It will give a 'section occupied' indication if there is a train in *any* section connected to the same controller, or if the controller output is negative or if the controller output presents a low resistance. Clearly, if the button is only pressed when the section is occupied, this anomalous behaviour will go unnoticed.

In sections where reversing is needed often it is preferable to use a more sophisticated type of track circuit. Unidirectional units, however, are quite useful on multiple-track main lines where most movements are forwards.

Chapter 9: Live-rail quasi-bidirectional track circuit

The live-rail unidirectional track circuit described in Chapter 8 has the advantage of simplicity but the disadvantage that a switch must be added if reversing is to be permitted. The occasions when this switch is used can, however, be defined in electrical terms as when both: (i) a train is in the section (and therefore the track circuit is activated) and (ii) the controller output is negative relative to the common return, ie it is set to reverse. This suggests that it should be possible to substitute the reversing switch (the type that shorts out the isolating diode) by a transistor of suitable rating which only conducts under the electrical conditions described above. So it behaves as an automatic reversing switch, anticipating the operator's use of the switch which it replaces. The resulting track circuit unit should be almost as useful as a fully bidirectional unit. Figure 9.1 gives the circuit diagram of a practical unit of this type, which I have described as a *quasi*-bidirectional track circuit.

How it works

The circuitry around T3/T4/T5 provides the automatic reversing facility. When a train is detected, T3 receives emitter bias from T1, stimulating collector current. Only when the controller output is negative, however, can diode D2 conduct, permitting T3's collector current to bias Darlington pair T4/T5 into conduction, providing a bypass around the isolation diode D1.

In practice this circuit presents difficulties and I warn prospective constructors that some experimentation, eg adjustment of component values, may be needed to make it work properly. The problem is that a high-current transistor such as T5, which must be a high-current type since the traction current for reversing trains passes through it, has sufficient internal capacitance to admit an appreciable pulse of negative-going current from the controller, even when unbiased. So, even when the section is vacant, such a

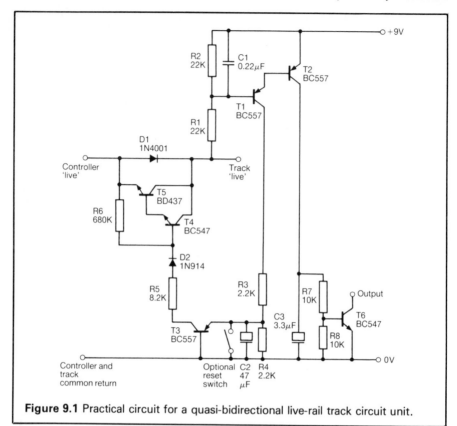

Figure 9.1 Practical circuit for a quasi-bidirectional live-rail track circuit unit.

pulse may pass through T5 biasing T1 into conduction. Now, if C2 were omitted, the pulse of collector current from T1 would bias T3 and, in turn, T4/T5 into conduction, whereupon controller output bypassing D1 would *continue* to activate T1 (and hence T3/T4/T5) causing a continuous 'section occupied' indication — although the section is vacant. This spurious indication would persist until the negative-going controller output is removed.

Capacitor C2, however, 'absorbs' the initial pulse of output from T1 before it can grow sufficiently to bias T3 into conduction. With a pulsed controller and in the absence of a train, C2 begins charging at the beginning of each pulse and discharges at the end of each pulse; T3 remains unconductive and no bias is supplied to T4/T5. The purpose of R6, whose value may need to be adjusted, is to kill spurious activation of T4/T5 by leakage current through T3 and D2. If there *is* a train in the section T1 conducts continuously, of course, so C2 becomes fully charged and the bypass system will operate if the controller is set to reverse.

Performance

In operation this quasi-bidirectional track circuit behaves like its unidirectional counterpart when the controller is set for forwards movement or is at 'stop', or is off. When set to reverse, the train will reverse with a slight but noticeable loss of power. If the train reverses out of the section, the 'section occupied' indication may persist until the controller setting is reduced.* This is because, once T4/T5 is conductive, the negative-going controller output continues to activate the track circuit, holding T4/T5 conductive.

You may wonder why with pulsed power the circuit does not reset itself between pulses once the train has left the section. The answer is that the same network (R3/R4/C2) which prevents the track circuit from being *activated* by such pulses of power also inevitably prevents it from being *de-activated* by the spaces between the pulses. One way of unlatching the system when it 'locks up' in this way is to add a normally-open push-button switch across R4/C2. When the 'section occupied' indication persists, push the button momentarily to discharge C2 and clear the spurious indication. An alternative is to replace the switch by an npn transistor biased from the output of the track circuit guarding the section entered by reversing trains. This type of track circuit is most useful in sections where most movement is forwards, with reverse movements being confined to short manoeuvres within the section. It is only marginally cheaper than a fully bidirectional live-rail common-return track circuit; compare Figure 9.1 with Figure 11.5. Nevertheless for certain situations the quasi-bidirectional unit is preferable and Appendix 2 shows how to choose the unit most suited for your application.

Chapter 10: Return-rail unidirectional (and quasi-bidirectional) track circuits

The track circuits described in Chapters 8 and 9 were described as *live-rail* track circuits because the track circuit input, ie the current that activates the track circuit in the presence of a train, is taken from the *live* rail (via R1 in Figure 8.4). There is, however, another kind of unidirectional track circuit in which the track circuit input is taken from the *return* rail. Figure 10.1 shows a possible circuit diagram.

It might, at first, seem that this kind of track circuit is of little more than academic importance because it is rather more extravagant in components than its live-rail counterpart and also because the track itself must normally be divided in *both* rails. The rail breaks, however, need not be opposite each other; those in the *return* rail now set the limits of the section. The rail breaks in the live rail may be used for other purposes, eg to define zones operated from different controllers. For certain applications, however, this kind of track circuit is very useful. For instance, it is possible to overlap blocks by using live-rail and return-rail track circuits alternately (see Chapter 15). Also a short return-rail section may be introduced *inside* a live-rail section (or *vice-versa*) where special 'point detection' is needed.

---

* With PWM controllers there is a critical pulse width below which the spuriously activated bypass system 'drops out'. This is a function of the network R1/R2/C1 which is intended to reduce the sensitivity of the track circuit to pulsed inputs — it works in the same way as the similar network R3/R4/C2.

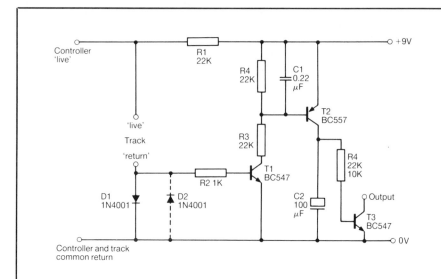

Figure 10.1 Return-rail unidirectional track circuit. D1 is the isolation diode. D2 is the optional reversing diode whose inclusion makes the track circuit quasi-bidirectional. With this circuit compare the classic 'twin-T' track circuit (Figure 11.1).

Operation

The performance of this track circuit is somewhat different from that of the live-rail type described earlier. This is because the track circuit input voltage, being taken now from the *return* rail, is limited to around 0.7 V by the isolation diode, which, of course, must now be on the return side of the track. The effect of this is to limit the sensitivity of the track circuit at lower settings of the controller. As the speed control is advanced, more current flows through the section (assuming it is occupied) and the voltage across the diode rises (although still around 0.7 V), increasing track circuit sensitivity. This is in contrast with the live-rail track circuit whose sensitivity falls as the controller is advanced.

Reversing could be allowed, as with the live-rail circuit, by using a double-pole double-throw switch to exchange connections to both rails in the section. Alternatively a single-pole switch could be used to short-circuit the isolation diode but this would also short-circuit the track circuit input, causing train detection to cease. Interestingly, however, the return-rail unidirectional track circuit can be made to permit reversing automatically by a very simple modification — adding a second high-current diode in reverse parallel with the isolation diode (this is shown in dotted lines as D2 in Figure 10.1). This modification converts the unit into a quasi-bidirectional type so when trains are running forward or are stationary D2 is reverse biased and so has no effect upon the circuit. When the controller is set to reverse (provided that there is a train in section), D2 conducts permitting the train to reverse normally. With a pulsed controller the track circuit will continue to function normally between pulses, so train detection will continue.

This type of track circuit is, then, almost bidirectional. Indeed it is only one component removed from the celebrated 'twin-T' bidirectional track circuit (Figure 11.1).

Chapter 11: Bidirectional track circuits

Bidirectional track circuits, as their name suggests, permit full bidirectional movement of trains and under all normal conditions provide consistently accurate train detection. As with all track circuit types, rail breaks are essential and the track circuit unit is wired into a feed to the section which it guards.

Bidirectional track circuits function by monitoring the current flowing into the section. Often this is the power current from the controller but to provide for occasions when there is no output from the controller, eg when it is set to 'stop' or is off or disconnected, the track circuit power supply voltage is also applied to the section via the track circuit unit's current detector. The current available from this power supply to the section, called the *auxiliary* current, is limited by a resistor to a maximum of a few milliAmps to prevent unwanted movement of trains. However, this auxiliary current is sufficient to activate the current detector in the track circuit unit ensuring that trains are detected under all prevailing conditions.

You may wonder whether train detection is interrupted when the controller output is equal and of opposite polarity to the auxiliary current. Theoretically, of course, this is possible and indeed one authority (James Kyle) suggests for this very reason that the auxiliary current be AC! In practice, however, with most controllers and a DC auxiliary current no such interruption occurs. This is because most controllers deliver a pulsed output which cannot cancel a steady direct current! Between pulses, train detection continues and practical circuits include smoothing to convert intermittent detection into a continuous 'section occupied' indication. What *can* happen with certain electronic controllers is that auxiliary current enters the controller's feedback-loop, where it can cause a number of interesting phenomena, which are described in detail in Appendix 2.

The 'twin-T' detector

The heart of a bidirectional track circuit is its current detector. This poses a knotty design problem since it must both pass and detect current of either polarity, from a few milliAmps to over 1A, without incurring a heavy voltage drop, which would adversely affect the performance of the trains. The easiest way to detect a current is to pass it through a resistor and to use the potential difference developed across this to bias a transistor into conduction. An ordinary resistor, however, could not cope with the wide range of currents encountered. For instance, to give the necessary minimum of 0.7 V at 10 mA (high for an auxiliary current) the resistor would need to be 68 Ω, but then at 250 mA (typical for an OO/HO-scale loco at cruising speed) the voltage drop would be an intolerable, if not impossible, 17 V. So, we need a special resistor which will adjust its resistance to suit the prevailing conditions — ideally one whose resistance is inversely proportional to the current flowing through it, so that the voltage drop is constant at around 0.7 V. At once the mental bells should ring for we have just described our old friend, the (forward-biased)

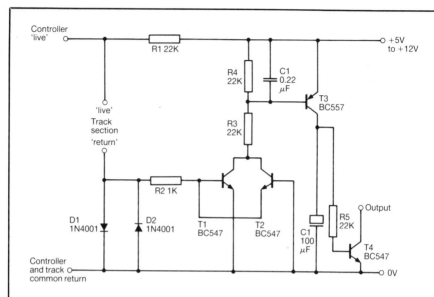

Figure 11.1 A bidirectional return-rail track circuit, a modern example of the 'twin-T' type detector first described by Linn Westcott in the 1950s, a classic in model railway electronics. For use with 0 gauge and above, D1 and D2 should be uprated to type 1N5401.

silicon diode. Yet, because it conducts in only one direction and because the controller output may be of either polarity, two such diodes must be used in reverse parallel, the so-called 'twin-T' arrangement.

One way to obtain a digital output, ie a two-state 'section occupied'/'section vacant' indication, from the voltage drop across the twin-T pair is to use this voltage as the input to a transistor amplifier. Since the voltage may be of either polarity, depending on the polarity of the current being detected, it is applied to the reverse-parallel base/emitter junctions of two transistors of the same polarity; their two collectors are bonded, so collector current from one transistor or the other (of uniform polarity of course) is stimulated by voltage drop of either polarity across the twin-T pair. Obviously, when the section is vacant, no current can flow into it, so there is no voltage drop across the twin-T pair and neither transistor conducts. A typical circuit of a practical twin-T unit is shown in Figure 11.1. Notice its similarity to the return-rail quasi-bidirectional track circuit described in Chapter 10.

Since the twin-T track circuit was first described by the American model railway writer Linn Westcott in 1958, it has, together with a multitude of variant circuits, become the most widely used kind of track circuit unit on model railways. Nevertheless, until recently the system was not widely known in the UK and the author's own EDOTIS (Electronic Detection of Trains In Sections), which is a twin-T variant, was developed quite independently in connection with *Practical Electronics for Railway Modellers*. In EDOTIS the twin-T pair itself is omitted, the entire traction current passing through the

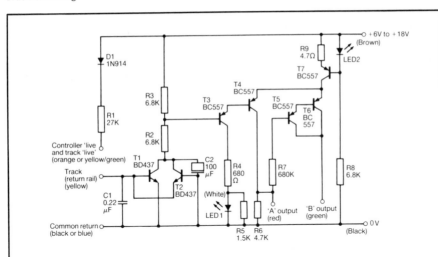

Figure 11.2 A 'twin-T' variant, the author's own EDOTIS, shown here connected for return-rail operation. Colour references are to the colours of the flying leads on the commercial version.

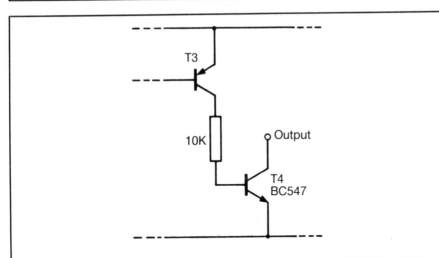

Figure 11.3 Circuit for converting the positive-going outputs of EDOTIS to TTL-compatible negative-going outputs.

base/emitter junction (which behaves like a diode) of one or other of the front-end transistor pair. Inevitably these transistors must be high-current types and both the BD437 and the MJE3055 have been used satisfactorily. The circuit diagram of the commercial version of EDOTIS is given in Figure 11.2. The current limiter circuit is optional and prevents damage to the output transistors by inadvertent short-circuiting of the output terminals. This unit's two antiphase outputs were originally intended for the direct driving of two-aspect signals; note that these outputs are not compatible with TTL. Figure 11.3 shows how EDOTIS outputs can be made TTL-compatible. EDOTIS, no longer in commercial production, is a rugged unit having high sensitivity and an excellent record for reliability.

As with unidirectional track circuits there is a choice of modes, live-rail and return-rail, in which a bidirectional track circuit may operate. Yet, as the live-rail mode poses certain difficulties, the current detector is positioned almost invariably in the *return* feed to the section, ie return-rail operation. As with unidirectional return-rail track circuits, the section is normally isolated in both rails, the breaks in the return rail defining the limits of the section. The breaks in the live rail need not be opposite the others and in some circumstances, eg only one controller in use, may be omitted altogether. The live rail may be differently divided into zones capable of being fed from separate controllers. This is perfectly satisfactory, provided that each control zone, if at any point it is opposite a track-circuited section of return rail, is connected to the positive terminal of the track circuit power supply via a suitable resistor to provide a source of auxiliary current. Since return-rail track circuits share the layout common return, any number of them may share the same power supply. The alternative arrangement places the current detector in the feed to the *live* rail and although this simplifies installation insofar as rail breaks are needed only in the live rail, terrible power supply complications may ensue. Since one of the track circuit input terminals is generally connected to the track circuit's common return, this will be inevitably at the same potential as the controller's *live* terminal and *not* that of the layout common return. On layouts having only one controller this poses no problem but if several controllers are in use their live terminals are likely to be at different potentials relative to the layout common return. This forces the use of separate track circuit power supplies, one in association with each controller, to serve the track circuit units connected to each. If track sections can be switched from one controller to another, their track circuits must be switched simultaneously between power supplies. Further complications arise where the outputs of several track circuits connected to different controllers are fed into the same unit, eg a three- or four-aspect signal driver. Such was the limitation of EDOTIS when used in the live-rail mode, but when used in the return-rail mode as shown in Figure 11.2 these difficulties disappear.

Live-rail, common-return bidirectional track circuit
One might be excused at this stage for dismissing the concept of the live-rail bidirectional track circuit as impractical. Indeed, as an alternative I developed the quasi-bidirectional live-rail track circuit (Chapter 9) which shares the layout's common return and therefore suffers no complications. Yet still for many applications a *fully* bidirectional live-rail track circuit sharing the layout's common return would be invaluable and its design presented a challenge that I found irresistible! The resulting unit, EDOTIS II, can be temperamental but the original prototype has now given years of satisfactory service on my layout, where, incidentally, it has overlap zones with return-rail EDOTIS units in the adjacent sections (see Chapter 15, especially Figure 15.1).

First, let us discover the reason for the 'live-rail problem'. Figure 11.4 shows a simplified EDOTIS front end reconfigured in an attempt at live-rail

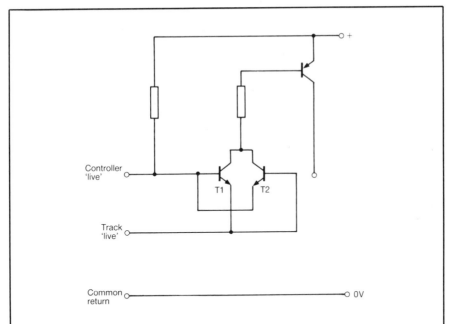

Figure 11.4 Simplified front end of an EDOTIS-type track circuit reconfigured for live-rail common-return operation. Reasons for its unsatisfactory performance are given in the text.

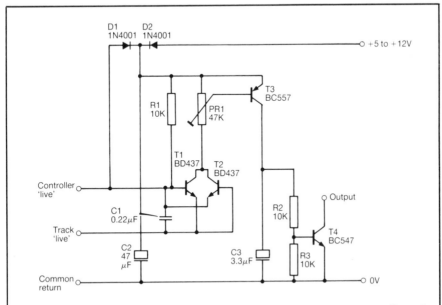

Figure 11.5 Circuit of EDOTIS II (also called TEKTOR), a common-return, live-rail track circuit unit.

common-return operation. Under some conditions this unit performs satisfactorily, but the problem arises when the controller output is positive and at a higher voltage than the track circuit power supply. The controller output now *forward biases* the base/collector junction of T1 and *reverse biases* T3's base/emitter junction, preventing train detection. In practice train detection in one direction fails at all but the very lowest speeds.

One solution would be to operate this track circuit from a power supply at a voltage higher than the controller can deliver but this would need to be at least 25 V, which is inconvenient for a number of reasons. There is, however, a more subtle means of achieving the same effect, while still retaining a more convenient track circuit supply voltage (5 to 12 V).

Most controllers deliver an output that is pulsed. This output of necessity contains peaks of voltage higher than the mean. We can arrange quite simply for these peaks to charge up a capacitor which is then used as an alternative power supply for the track circuit's front end. Since this alternative supply voltage will approach the *peak* controller output voltage, it will be inevitably higher than the *mean* controller voltage, enabling train detection to continue. The front end's output will, on occasion, consist of pulses but later smoothing can convert this into a continuous 'section occupied' indication.

The complete circuit diagram of a track circuit unit which employs these principles is given in Figure 11.5. The juxtaposition of diodes D1 and D2 and capacitor C2 ensures that the front end takes as its power supply whichever of the track circuit power supply and the controller peak output offers the higher,

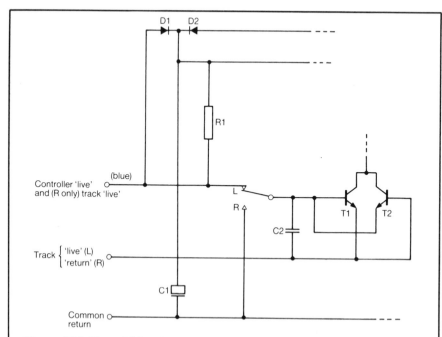

Figure 11.6 The additional of a SPDT switch to the front end of EDOTIS II provides the versatility of live-rail *or* return-rail operation.

ie more positive, output, since the higher voltage will forward bias the adjacent diode and reverse bias the other.

This track circuit functions satisfactorily under most normal operating conditions. Only if the controller delivers a steady DC more positive than the track circuit power supply, eg in a pure DC controller or when certain types of PWM controller are set to maximum speed, train detection may fail. The solution in a pure DC controller is to superimpose an audio frequency signal (Chapter 30) or in a PWM controller to reduce the controller setting until pulsing, and therefore train detection, is resumed. With controllers operating from unsmoothed power supplies, eg the controller described in Chapter 1, there are no such problems.

Figure 11.6 shows a simple modification to EDOTIS II's front end to enable it to operate as either a live-rail or a return-rail track circuit, as selected on a single-pole double-throw switch which greatly enhances its usefulness. Note that in either mode the blue lead is connected to the live output terminal of the controller, the yellow lead to the track-circuited rail and the black lead to the layout common-return.

Capacitor C1 kills spurious detection caused by pulsed power charging and discharging the residual capacitance between the rails. The presence of a locomotive or other conductive vehicle in the section will always cause either T1 or T2 to become conductive, the combined collector currents in PR1 raising bias for T3. The setting of PR1 is critical. If too high, spurious detection may result, if too low detection by auxiliary current may fail, especially on low supply voltages. Capacitor C3 in the collector circuit of T3 provides smoothing of the 'section occupied' indication, which is essential for most applications, especially in signalling. Each pulse of output from the front end charges C3, which takes appreciable time (0.33 ms) to discharge via R2 and so has still retained most of its charge when it is replenished by the next pulse.

Appendix 2: Operation and choice of track circuits

What track circuits detect

A track circuit could be defined as a system that provides an electrical indication when the continuity of a section of track is completed by the presence of rail vehicles. As mentioned earlier, most model rolling stock, being designed for use on two-rail track, is non-conductive and therefore has no effect on track circuits unless modified as described below. Model locomotives, however, generally are conductive by virtue of their motor windings and are detected by track circuits without needing any modification. You may find that detection of locomotives alone is sufficient for your needs, but read Chapter 15 on the problem of overlap.

One type of locomotive that may not be detected by a track circuit is an electric-outline loco drawing its power from an overhead catenary or a third rail. If your layout uses either of these systems of electrification, you must ensure that your track circuits are all return-rail types. If you use live-rail track circuits these will have to be duplicated in the overhead or third-rail feeds. Alternatively, you will need to modify the locomotive to ensure that it activates the live-rail track circuits, as described below.

Vehicles fitted with lights that operate from the controller output will also be detected by track circuits. Vehicles fitted with lights intended to operate only from a high-frequency lighting system (Chapter 27) and having blocking capacitors in series with the lamps will only be detected while the high-frequency generator is operating. Vehicles fitted with speakers for through-the-rails sound (Chapter 30) will be detected while the sound system is on. In fact, such vehicles may be *temporarily* detected when the lighting or sound system is off and while the auxiliary current charges up the blocking capacitors. I have also seen HF lit stock detected by EDOTIS II-type track circuits when the controller is on but the HF unit off. EDOTIS II is a very sensitive unit and will detect the charge/discharge of the blocking capacitors under pulsed power even at frequencies too low to light the lamps.

Any vehicle can be modified to activate track circuits by making it suitably conductive. The sensitivity of track circuits varies widely, depending on such factors as track circuit type, supply voltage and controller setting. If you wish to 'conductivise' a vehicle, I advise you to try placing various resistors across the track, testing at all settings of the controller, forwards and reverse, in order to determine the highest resistance that is detected under all conditions likely to be encountered. Start with 1 K.

There are three ways of 'conductivising' stock and all demand that the vehicle be fitted with metal-tyred wheels. Firstly, solder a suitable resistor from a spoke on one wheel to the corresponding spoke on the opposite wheel or, alternatively, fit power pickups and connect these to a resistor mounted in or beneath the vehicle. The third alternative is to paint over the insulating bushes or spokes with electrically conductive silver paint (available from model shops) and, when dry, brush off the excess to raise the resistance to the required value. If, when using the first two methods, a 1 K resistor is used, it should be rated for 0.5 W. If a lower value is used it should be rated 1 W.

Fault finding

Track circuiting is very reliable and, in general, trouble free but it is advisable to be aware of the possible causes when they apparently do not work as they ought.

Spurious detection, ie a 'section occupied' indication in the *absence* of a train, is rare, but if observed, check the following: all wiring and pointwork (especially if you use live-frog turnouts); check for mains leads in proximity to the track and wiring, which can cause interference; check for damp in the ballast and, if suspected, spray the track with automotive water repellent; also check if some other electrical system is in use which may interfere with track circuits. For example, the RELCO track cleaning device and high-frequency coach lighting systems both cause spurious detection with EDOTIS II. If you use RELCO, have a track cleaning session first, then switch the RELCO off for your operating session. If you make your own track using copper-clad board for sleepers (ties), examine the gaps in the copper for stray particles of metal causing a partial short circuit; I have seen this cause spurious detection on a club layout.

Nil detection, ie absence of a 'section occupied' indication in the *presence* of a train is more common than the opposite fault and may be caused by many factors. Check the following: cleanliness of the track and loco wheels, power pickups, motor brushes and commutator. Check the track circuit power supply: short-circuit the track and see if this gives a 'section occupied' indication. The use of filament lamps as status indicators wired across the controller output should be avoided, unless you use only unidirectional live-rail track circuits; these lamps when off have a very low resistance which short-circuits the auxiliary current. As status indicators use LEDs (with series resistors, of course) which cause no such adverse effects. The same effect occurs if a controller is connected to a number of zones, some of which are track-circuited and some not; a stationary locomotive in a non-track-circuited zone will short-circuit auxiliary current so that a conductive vehicle in a track-circuited zone will not be registered while the controller is at stop. Similarly a loco stopped so that it is partially in a track-circuited zone and partially in a non-track-circuited zone will not be detected, but, if it is parked so that it straddles two track-circuited zones, it will normally be registered in both.

Mutual interference is caused, unfortunately, when track circuits are used with certain types of electronic controller, eg as in Chapter 4, because auxiliary current enters the controller's feedback loop. This causes a variety of fascinating phenomena such as nil detection, slowing of trains in track-circuited sections, speeding of trains in track-circuited sections and even inability to bring trains to a complete stop (in one direction). The cure for this is to modify the *controller* by the addition of a 4.7 K resistor in parallel with the output transistor to provide a leakage current that 'swamps' the auxiliary current and is not itself controlled by the feedback loop.

Selection of track circuit type

Your choice of track circuit type will be influenced by three factors: (i) the kind of operations taking place in the section; (ii) the system of electrification; and (iii) expense. The following guide should help you choose the appropriate track circuit for your situation.

1 Does your section carry traffic in both directions or in one direction only? If both directions, go to (2) below; if one direction, go to (4) below.

2 Do you use (or intend to use) high-frequency train lighting? If so, use only return-rail bidirectional track circuits. Otherwise go to (3) below.

3 Does your controller deliver a steady or a pulsed output? If steady, do you use through-the-rails sound? If not, use only return-rail bidirectional track circuits. Otherwise use return-rail or live-rail bidirectional track circuits, as convenient.

4 Do you use (or intend to use) high-frequency train lighting? If not, proceed to (5) below. If so, is your controller output (relative to the common return) positive or negative? If positive, use a return-rail unidirectional track circuit. If negative, use a return-rail *bidirectional* track circuit.

5 Is your controller output (relative to the common return) positive or negative? If positive proceed to (6) below. If negative, use a live-rail or return-rail *bidirectional* track circuit.

6 Does your controller deliver a steady or a pulsed output? If steady, do you use through-the-rails sound? If not, use a return-rail unidirectional track circuit. Otherwise, use a live-rail unidirectional track circuit.

Part 4

Signalling systems

Prologue

Throughout Parts 4 and 5 the vocabulary of prototype signalling is employed in regard to the positions of trains relative to signals. This may take a little understanding. Imagine that you are a train driver looking out of your cab at the line in front of you. Everything in front of you is said to be *in advance* of you. Everything behind you is *in rear*. So far so good. If your train has just passed a signal, that signal is now *in rear* but if we are standing beside the signal watching the train disappear into the distance, we say that the train is *in advance* of the signal or *inside* the signal. A second train approaching the signal is said to be *in rear* of it. So, *in advance* always means further on in the normal direction of travel, while *in rear* always means further back, contrary to the normal direction of travel. Readers wanting a detailed account of UK signalling practice (which is not greatly different from much North American practice) are recommended to read *British Railway Signalling* by G.M. Kichenside and Alan Williams (Ian Allan).

Introduction

A working signalling system adds a lot to a layout. The sight of a colour light signal changing automatically as a train passes, or as a loco is unprototypically placed on the track by an out-of-scale hand, gives a layout a feeling of 'life' that has to be seen to be believed. Now it's no longer just the trains that are doing things.

Once track circuiting (Part 3) has been installed, automatic signalling follows quite easily. Only semaphore signals pose problems; their automatic operation is considered in Project 22 of *Practical Electronics for Railway Modellers* and Chapter 16 of this book. The simplest two-aspect colour light signals can be driven direct from track circuits that are fitted with antiphase pairs of outputs (as in Figure 11.2) but, as Chapter 15 points out, such a system, however effective, may still fall short of prototype practice unless overlap is provided. The more interesting three- and four-aspect signals need their own drive units which take inputs from the track circuits on two or three adjacent blocks. An interesting variation is to model a manually operated signal which spends most of its life showing the danger aspect and is cleared by the signalman only on the approach of a train. This too can be simulated electronically, the signal drive unit taking inputs from the approach track circuits as well as those in advance.

While it is possible to construct even the most complex signal drive units using discrete transistors and diodes (suggested circuits are given in *Practical Electronics for Railway Modellers*) the units in this book use TTL, ie transistor/transistor logic integrated circuits. These greatly simplify construction and reduce costs. A four-aspect signal drive unit, for instance, can be constructed using only the 7400 and 7432 ICs (about 20p each), and the four LEDs (light-emitting diodes) that serve as signal aspects. You will need a stabilised 5 V power supply for your TTL signalling system and you may find that this voltage is too low for your track circuit units, in which case these will need a separate supply. This will not matter providing that the negative terminals of both supplies are returned to the layout common return. For a detailed description of TTL see Appendix 4. Track circuit units for use with these systems must give a TTL-compatible logic '0' when the section is occupied.

Another difference between the signalling systems described in this book and those in *Practical Electronics for Railway Modellers* is that all signal aspects are assumed to be LEDs. There are many reasons for this: (i) modern LEDs are much brighter and have stronger colour than is available from grain-of-wheat bulbs; (ii) the best LEDs are available in 'water clear' transparent epoxy resin encapsulations, which enhance the realism of non-illuminated aspects; (iii) LEDs run cold and so do not cause melting or distortion in plastics or white metal structures; (iv) LEDs are not prone to catastrophic failure provided they are used within their limits. Their brightness fades only very gradually. Modern types have a half life (ie time for brightness to fall to 50 per cent) of 100 operating years! (v) T1¾-size LEDs are 5 mm in diameter, ideal for use in 7 mm scale models. T1-size LEDS are 3 mm in diameter, ideal for use in 4 mm scale models. Smaller-size LEDs are available, which may suit those modelling in even smaller scales; (vi) LEDs consume little power — I have read a newspaper by the light of a T1-size extra-bright red LED drawing less than 10 mA (and my night vision is said to be worse than average!) and (vii) LEDs can be driven direct from TTL outputs.

LEDs are now available in all primary colours so it should not be long before they are available in every conceivable hue. Red LEDS are ideally suited as red aspects of signals. Some green LEDs, however, give a yellowish green that is less than ideal but is nevertheless better than the green available from grain-of-wheat bulbs. They are quite acceptable as green aspects but the blue LEDs that are now becoming available give a greenish blue that may be preferable as a green aspect.* Signal yellow is, in fact, amber though always called yellow by signalmen; amber LEDs are available, but make sure that they *are* amber; orange types are almost indistinguishable from red, while yellow types are nearly green. (Some amber LEDs are sold as yellow LEDs.) Multicolour LEDs are now readily available, and these are ideally suited for use in model searchlight signals (see Project 26 in *Practical Electronics for Railway Modellers*). LEDs must be handled and used carefully. They are easily damaged by excessive heat when soldering, by excessive current or inverse

*A difficulty with blue LEDs is their higher operating voltage quoted as 7 V, although I have seen them operating satisfactorily from 5 V TTL supplies.

voltages. To protect against inverse voltages, always *either* connect the cathode (identified generally as the lead adjacent to a flat on the lip of the device) to the most negative part of the circuit *or* connect the anode to the most positive part of the circuit. To limit the current through the LED there must be sufficient resistance in series with the device. The general formula for the series resistance is $R = (E-2)/I$ when R is the series resistance in Ohms, E is the supply voltage and I is the maximum required current in Amps. For most LEDs a suitable value for I is 0.02 (20 mA). When driving LEDs from TTL outputs, however, complications arise because the integrated circuits themselves include series resistors (nominally 130 Ω) and sometimes series diodes as well. In the circuits given in this book an 82 Ω resistor is included in series with LEDs driven between the outputs and the negative rail. This is not only to limit the current, but also to allow the output voltage to rise sufficiently high to be recognised as a logical '1', when the output also forms the input to another gate. When LEDs are connected between the output and the positive rail, rather higher series resistors are needed.

Chapter 12: Basic colour-light signalling systems

This Chapter is concerned with 'basic' automatic colour-light signalling systems (two-, three- and four-aspect), ie signals controlled only by track circuit occupation. Remember that we are committed, as far as possible, to the use of TTL for signal driver circuits and to the use of track circuit units that give a TTL-compatible logic '0' output when a train is detected and to the use of LEDs as signal aspects.

As an alternative to track circuit units, bistables operated by reed switches, isolated lengths of rail or check rails (see Projects 15 and 16 in *Practical Electronics for Railway Modellers*) could be used to provide inputs to the signal drivers. If the bistables use npn transistors, a logical '0' will be available from the collector of the transistor that is conductive. As a further alternative, bistables can be made using pairs of the NAND gates on the 7400/74LS00 IC as shown in Figure 12.1. These bistables require a '0' pulse on their inputs. Input 1 drives the bistable into its 'occupied' state whereupon a '1' is available on output 1 and a '0' on output 2. A '0' on input 2 returns the bistable to its 'vacant' state when a '0' is given on output 1 and a '1' on output 2. Two such

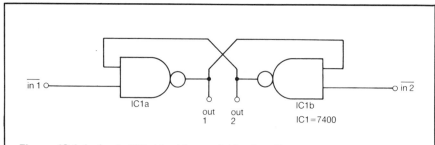

Figure 12.1 A simple TTL bistable, useful in signalling systems.

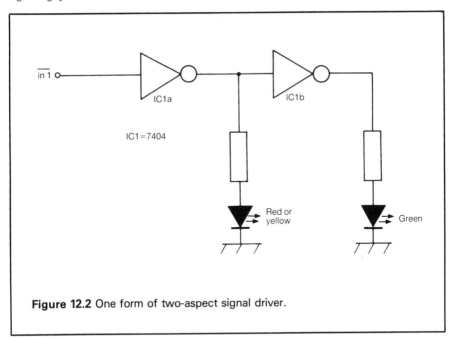

Figure 12.2 One form of two-aspect signal driver.

bistables can be made using each IC. However, these bistables in the noisy electrical environment of a working model railway are somewhat prone to spurious changes of state. Circuits for each type of signal are given first assuming the use of discrete LEDs as aspects in a common cathode configuration. Often the LEDs can be used as substitutes for 'grain-of-wheat' bulbs in proprietary signals.

Secondly this Chapter describes the corresponding searchlight signal type using a three-lead common-*anode* multicolour LED. Unfortunately the excellent unit that used to be available from Maplin Electronic Supplies Ltd (catalogue number YY61R) has now been deleted. Details of the construction of searchlight signals using this type of device are given in Project 26 of *Practical Electronics for Railway Modellers*.

Two-aspect signals

Two-aspect are the simplest signals, showing two colours (aspects) only. A 'home' or 'stop' signal guards a block or a junction and shows 'danger' (red) when the line is not clear and 'clear' (green) at other times. A 'distant' or 'repeater' stands some way in rear of a stop signal to give the train driver warning of the aspect of the stop signal which he is approaching. It shows 'caution' (yellow) when the stop signal is at 'danger' and green at other times.

On model railways, blocks tend to be short, so a prototypical two-aspect signalling system with stop signals and repeaters is likely to result in a superabundance of signals but if you have the space to create long blocks a two-aspect system does offer electrical simplicity. Figure 12.2 shows one possible driver circuit using a pair of inverters in the 7404 or 74LS04 IC (better switching characteristics will be obtained with the 7414 or 74LS14.) A simpler circuit can be used if you are willing to adopt a common-anode configuration, as shown in Figure 12.3 but this system is not compatible with the other systems described in this book.

If you are using section bistables based on the 7400 IC you can eliminate the series resistors and connect the LEDs in reverse parallel between the two outputs of the bistable. Connect additional signals in series with the first. Reverse the connections to any signal that persistently shows the wrong aspect. If you are modelling searchlight signals and using a common-anode multicolour LED, a different approach is needed. Suitable drivers for home and distant signals are shown in Figure 12.4.

Three-aspect signals

A three-aspect signal combines the functions of stop and repeater signals by displaying three possible aspects: 'danger' (red) if the block being guarded is unavailable; 'caution' (yellow) if the block being guarded is clear but the next block in advance is unavailable (ie the next signal is at 'danger'); and 'clear' (green) only if the block being guarded *and* the next block in advance are both clear. Three-aspect signalling is probably the most promising system for use on model railways, since it offers interest without dense packing of signals or the use of very long runs. For use with discrete LEDs the simplest driver circuit is probably that shown in Figure 12.5, which uses the 7402 or 74LS02 quadruple two-input NOR gate IC. A NOR gate provides a logical '1' output only if there is a '0' on *all* its inputs; in all other circumstances it gives a '0' output. IC1a is used as an inverter only. A '0' on input 1 drives its output high, lighting the red LED and also providing a '1' at one input of both IC1b and IC1c, ensuring the other two aspects are extinguished.

If the red is off, a logical '0' on input 2 will give a '1' at the output of IC1b, lighting the yellow LED. It also passes on a '1' to one input of IC1c, holding the green off. Only when both red and yellow aspects are off (because there are no '0's on either driver input) will both inputs of IC1c be '0's, causing the green LED to light. The unit therefore gives true three-aspect logic.

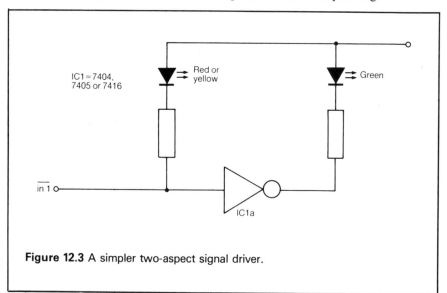

Figure 12.3 A simpler two-aspect signal driver.

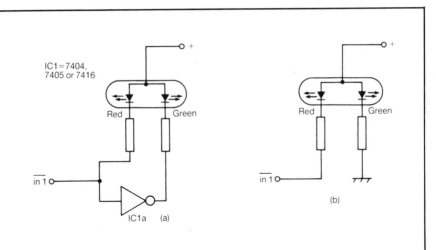

Figure 12.4 Two-aspect searchlight signal driver circuits for common-anode multicolour LEDs: **(a)** stop signal; **(b)** repeater signal.

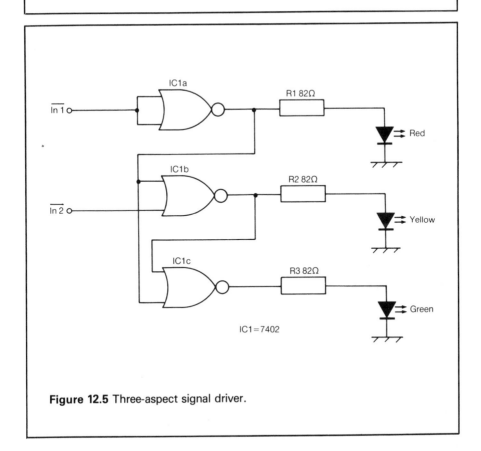

Figure 12.5 Three-aspect signal driver.

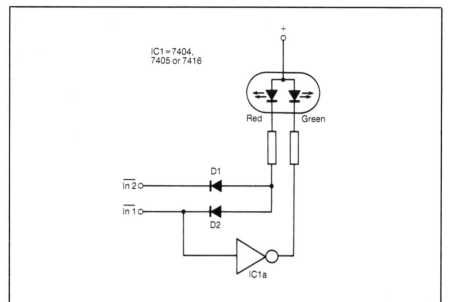

Figure 12.6 Three-aspect signal driver using common-anode multicolour LED.

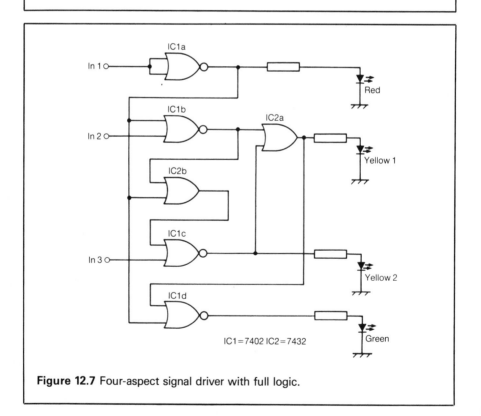

Figure 12.7 Four-aspect signal driver with full logic.

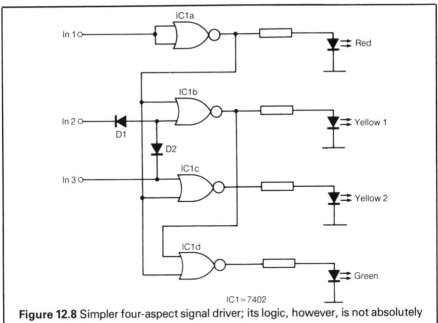

Figure 12.8 Simpler four-aspect signal driver; its logic, however, is not absolutely correct.

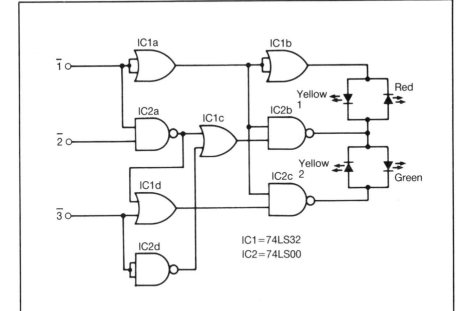

Figure 12.9 Four-aspect signal driver in which the signal needs only a three-wire connection.

The 7402 IC contains *four* NOR gates so if you use one IC per signal driver there will be a spare gate in each IC. It is recommended that this be connected with both its inputs to the positive rail. Alternatively, you may be able to use this gate as a gate or inverter in some other part of your signalling system. Do not leave the gate with its inputs unconnected. A three-aspect driver for a searchlight signal using a common-anode multicolour LED can be constructed as in Figure 12.6.

Four-aspect signals

A four-aspect signal in standard UK practice resembles a three-aspect signal with the additional double yellow aspect providing a 'preliminary caution' which indicates that the next two blocks in advance are clear, but not the third block. The 'clear' indication (green) on a four-aspect signal means that the next *three* (at least) blocks are clear. On a model railway you need a long continuous run of at least four blocks, to justify the installation of a four-aspect system.

Using discrete LEDs the circuit shown in Figure 12.7 provides full four-aspect logic. Note that it uses an entire 7402 (quad NOR) IC and half a 7432 (quad OR). If stringent economies are the order of the day I suggest that you build the drivers in pairs with the 7432 shared between each pair. The circuit works much as that of Figure 12.5 except that IC2b and IC1c combine to behave as a three-input NOR gate giving a '1' output only when there are '0's on the outputs of IC1a and IC1b and on input 3. IC2a provides for the yellow 1 aspect to be illuminated when *either* the single yellow *or* the double yellow is required, as on the prototype. If the full-logic driver in Figure 12.7 is too complex there is a simpler circuit using only the 7402 and two diodes. Strictly, Schottky diodes ought be used for their low voltage drop but the circuit works well with inexpensive *germanium* diodes (my prototype used OA47s). The

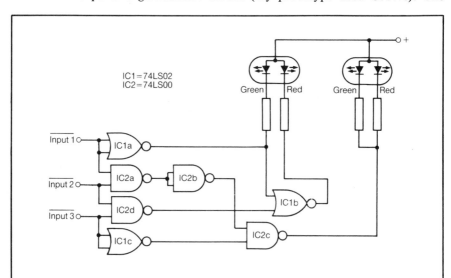

Figure 12.10 Driver circuit for a four-aspect searchlight signal using common-anode multicolour LEDs.

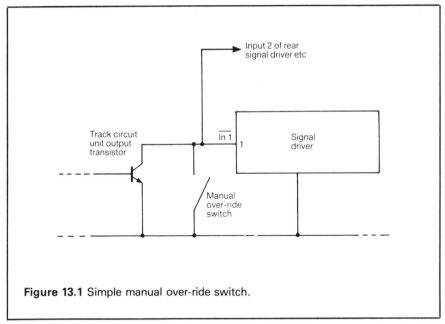

Figure 13.1 Simple manual over-ride switch.

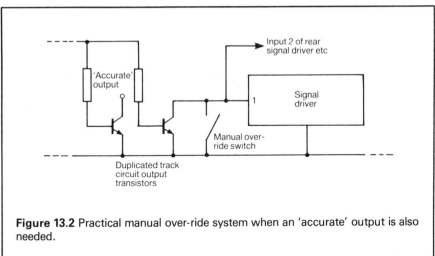

Figure 13.2 Practical manual over-ride system when an 'accurate' output is also needed.

circuit is given in Figure 12.8. However, this circuit falls short of correct four-aspect logic insofar as a '0' on input 2 does *not* inhibit the double-yellow indication. Thus, if '0's are applied to inputs 2 and 3 simultaneously, the signal will display double yellow instead of the single yellow that is strictly correct but, unless you run a very intensive train service with a train in almost every block, this shortcoming is unlikely to be noticed.

Figure 12.9 shows yet another alternative circuit for driving a four-aspect signal. This driver provides full four-aspect logic and is rather elegant since the signal needs only a three-wire connection and no other components are used besides the 7400 and 7432 ICs. The circuit makes good use of the push-pull output capabilities of TTL, the internal series resistor in the positive output path of each gate being used to limit the current. A further four-aspect signal driver circuit is given in Appendix 4 (see Figure A4.9).

Four-aspect searchlight signals are confined to a few locations in the UK, such as parts of the East Coast Main Line around Darlington and Newcastle and on parts of the former London, Tilbury and Southend Railway network from London's Fenchurch Street terminus. (The East side of London is currently a signal enthusiast's paradise with almost every conceivable type of colour-light signal in use.) On a four-aspect searchlight signal the lower lens displays the normal red, yellow and green aspects. The upper lens displays yellow only and is only illuminated when the double yellow aspect is required.

Figure 12.10 shows a driver circuit for a four-aspect searchlight signal using a pair of common-anode multicolour LEDs. Consideration of this circuit will show that it gives full four-aspect logic. This time a whole 7400 (quad two-input NAND) and most of a 7402 (quad two-input NOR) are used. The circuit diagram shows two multicolour LEDs in the signal, but you can save some expense by making the upper LED a water-clear amber LED of suitable size. Some adjustment of resistor values will be needed, however, to obtain a reasonable match of the two yellow aspects in terms of both hue and brightness.

Chapter 13: Manual over-ride

In prototype automatic signalling systems — as in the model signalling systems described in Chapter 12 — the signals clear automatically as the trains vacate the blocks being guarded. On prototype railways, however, there are occasions when the signalman needs to stop a train even though the line is clear. For example, there may be a fallen tree, a subsidence, or even — as I discovered once on a visit to Rugby Power Box — damage by vandals to the signalling system itself. For this reason UK legislation demands that a certain proportion of automatic signals be fitted with *manual over-ride,* that is, a system whereby the signalman can over-ride the automatic system and set the designated signal to danger and, of course, the one or two signals in rear of it to caution aspects as appropriate.

On a model railway manual over-ride is similarly invaluable on certain signals, and not simply with the aim of emulating prototype practice, worthy though that may be. A facility to set a signal to danger forms the basis of simulated manual signalling (Chapter 14), signalling at junctions (Chapter 18) and some forms of overlap (Chapter 15).

The signal driver circuit — and this applies equally to all the circuits described in Chapter 12 — sets the signal to danger when a logical '0' is applied to input 1. Normally this '0' comes from the track circuit unit or block bistable. In manual over-ride we 'trick' the signal driver into thinking that block 1 is occupied, even though it is not. The easiest way to do this is to connect a single-pole single-throw switch in parallel with the track circuit unit's output transistor, as shown in Figure 13.1. Closing the switch short-circuits this transistor, giving the same effect as if a train were detected. So, a logical '0' is presented to the signal driver input and the signal goes to danger

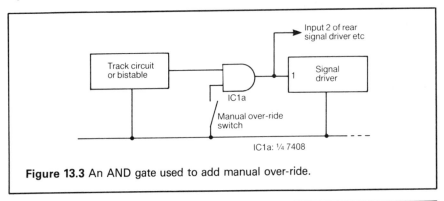

Figure 13.3 An AND gate used to add manual over-ride.

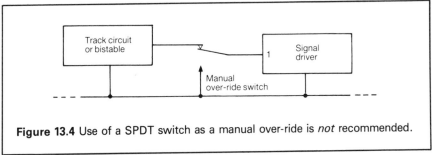

Figure 13.4 Use of a SPDT switch as a manual over-ride is *not* recommended.

but, and it's a big but, there are many circumstances in which you cannot use this simple arrangement. For instance, (i) you cannot use it if the train detector involves a bistable using NAND gates. You should avoid short-circuiting to ground the output of any TTL device, unless it has open-collector outputs. Even if your bistables use the 7401 or 7403 ICs which have open-collector outputs, your manual over-ride switch will interfere with the bistable action, so that the signal will not necessarily clear when the manual over-ride is removed and (ii) you cannot use it on a track circuit output if that output is also required to feed some other system which demands consistently accurate block occupation information, such as a 'block occupied' indicator LED or a progressive cab control (Chapter 26) unit. Closing the switch would, of course, light the LED although the block is vacant and might trick the progressive cab control (PCC) unit into connecting a controller to a vacant block. What you must do is to distinguish between the 'accurate' track circuit output needed by the indicator and the PCC unit and the 'vulnerable' input to the signal driver. Also, you must keep these two signal paths separate, so the latter cannot interfere with the former.

There are two ways in which this can be done:

(a) If the track circuit unit is easily accessible and if there is room on its circuit board, give it a second output transistor in parallel with the first. You will need to duplicate its bias resistor as well (see Figure 13.2). Now you have two identical and separate track circuit outputs, one of which may be dedicated to 'accurate' indications and the other for the 'vulnerable' feed to the signal driver, complete with manual over-ride switch.

(b) If the above is not feasible, or even if it is, consider instead inserting an

AND gate between the 'accurate' track circuit (or bistable) output and the signal driver input. Connect the manual over-ride switch between the other input of the AND gate and ground, as in Figure 13.3. Closing the switch will put a '0' on that input of the gate, ensuring that it delivers a '0' to the signal driver, whatever the state of the other input. When the switch is open, of course, the track circuit (or bistable) will drive the signal driver normally.

Note that for many reasons (b) is preferable. For instance, we could use a three-input AND gate. This gives us a spare input on which the application of a logical '0' will set the signal to danger. If our signal were at a trailing junction this third input might be related to the setting of the turnout (points) receiving a '0' when the turnout is set against the approaching train. See Chapter 18 for further information. For another system of manual over-ride applicable to signals at running junctions see Chapter 18.

You may well wonder what is wrong with the simple system shown in Figure 13.4, in which a single-pole double-throw switch applies a '0' to the signal drive input without affecting the track circuit or bistable output. It's fine in theory, but you may find that in practice it is less than satisfactory, especially with bistables. The reason is that this arrangement is liable to introduce more noise into the system but try it by all means if you wish.

If your signals are three- or four-aspect types, the input 2 to the signal driver in rear of that being over-ridden *must* be taken directly from input 1 of the over-ridden signal driver, so that the over-ride will set the signal in rear to yellow. So, too, if your signals are four-aspect types, the input 3 to the signal driver next-but-one in rear must be similarly derived. The connection to signal drivers in rear is shown in Figures 13.1, 13.2 and 13.3.

Chapter 14: Simulated manual signalling

Even to a casual observer of prototype railways there is a fundamental difference between the behaviour of automatic signals and manually operated ones. Automatic signals, as we noted in Chapter 13, clear automatically to green as the trains vacate the blocks being guarded. Consequently, even on intensely trafficked lines, automatic signals generally spend most of the time at green. Manually operated signals, on the other hand, spend most of the time at danger (or caution if two-aspect repeaters). They are only cleared by the signalman when he is expecting a train (assuming of course that the line is clear).

We could simulate a manual signalling system by giving every signal a manual over-ride (Chapter 13) and releasing the over-ride switches by hand whenever a train approaches a signal. However, that would be tedious and it is quite easy to arrange for the track circuits in *rear* of a signal to pull off an otherwise permanent 'manual over-ride'. The signal now *behaves* like a manual signal, although its operation is in fact automatic; this is why I call this 'simulated manual signalling'. Figure 14.1 shows the unit which must be added between the track circuit unit (or bistable) for the block being guarded and the signal driver, which may be any of the driver circuits in Chapter 12. The unit uses the three-input NAND gates in the 7410 IC, although IC1c is used as an inverter only. Indeed IC1b and IC1c together behave like a three-input AND gate. As shown in the Figure, the unit clears the signal when there is a train in

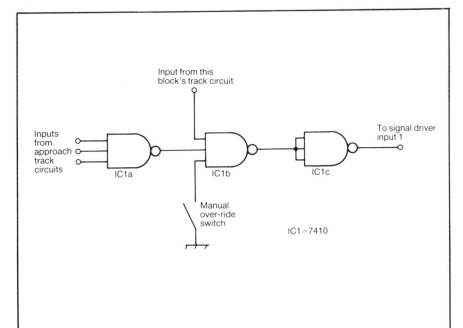

Figure 14.1 Simulated manual signalling.

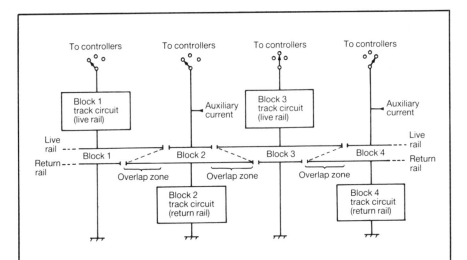

Figure 15.1 Alternate-rail track circuiting. By staggering the rail breaks blocks can be made to overlap to give prototypical protection even when locomotives only are detected.

any of the *three* track circuits on the approach to the signal. If you wish to modify this to the *two* or even *one* block in rear of the signal, simply connect the spare inputs of IC1a to the supply *positive* rail via a 10 K resistor. A manual over-ride is shown on one input to IC1b.

Chapter 15: Overlapping of blocks

In model railway signalling there is a very cogent reason for incorporating some form of *overlap*. Often a model train will consist of a locomotive, which, of course, is detected by track circuits, pulling unmodified rolling stock which remains undetected. Without overlap a train whose locomotive has just entered a block will trail into the previous block in which it is not detected and therefore unprotected. If the blocks are short, as they often are on model railways, spectators will be presented with the sight of coaches or wagons inside a signal showing a proceed aspect — and that just does not look right. An *overlap* system ensures that, when needed, there are at least two danger signals protecting the train. This makes signal operation more authentic and, if you use interlock (Chapter 23), the protection is more complete.

There are three ways in which overlap may be provided:

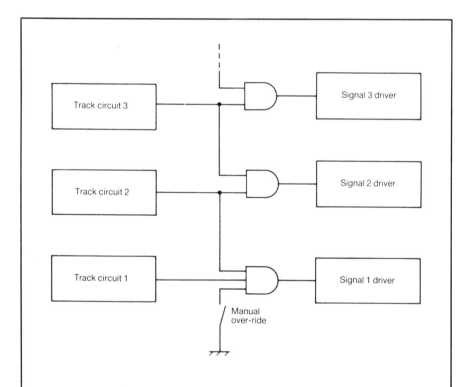

Figure 15.2 'Double blocking': AND gates are used to hold each signal at danger while the train is in either of two blocks. A manual over-ride has been fitted to signal 1, demanding the use of a three-input AND gate.

Alternate-rail track circuiting

In Part 3 we saw that there are two modes, live-rail and return-rail, in which track circuits operate and that the limits of a live-rail track-circuited section are defined by rail breaks in the live-rail and those of a return-rail track-circuited section by rail breaks in the return rail. If, therefore, successive blocks use live-rail and return-rail track circuits alternately, by careful staggering of the rail breaks as shown in Figure 15.1 it is possible to make adjacent blocks overlap; when in an overlap zone a train will be detected by *both* circuits.

A consequence of this is that, while in an overlap zone, a loco will suffer two 0.7 V drops, one from each track circuit. In practice this generally makes little difference to the performance of trains, especially with PWM controllers. With closed-loop controllers, however, a slight loss of speed, especially at low speed control settings, may be noticeable. One other problem arises if track circuits overlap in a zone connected to a controller having a diode across its output terminals, as in Chapters 1 to 4. When the controller is at 'stop', or is off, this diode is either forward biased or reverse biased by the source of auxiliary current, depending on the setting of the direction-change switch. If

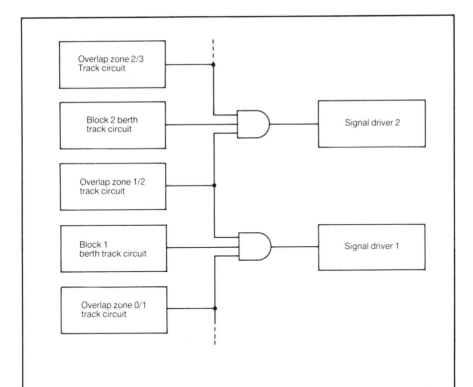

Figure 15.3 Overlap zone track circuiting. AND gates are used to ensure that each signal driver receives an input from its own berth track circuit and both adjacent overlap zones.

the diode is reverse biased, it will, of course, have no effect on the track circuit but if forward biased it will limit the track circuit voltage to about 0.7 V which is insufficient to activate the two track circuits in series. So, if a train is stopped in an overlap zone, on one setting of the direction control, train detection will fail. The solution is to modify the controller by adding a second diode in series with the first. This diode, which serves to protect the controller against the effects of inductive overshoot, has no effect on the operation of track circuits used singly. It is in parallel with the twin-T pair or the base/emitter junctions of the front-end pair of transistors.

Double blocking

This term was originally applied in prototype signalling to the practice of giving additional protection to high-speed trains by clearing the signals only when there were at least *two* clear blocks in advance. The model version, however, works retrospectively by ensuring that there are always at least *two* signals at danger behind the locomotive. The simplest way to provide double blocking is to feed each signal driver's input 1 from the outputs of *two* track circuits — the one guarding the block being signalled and the other guarding the next block in advance. Use AND gates to parallel the feeds; this will prevent interference between the track circuit outputs; see Figure 15.2.

Overlap-zone track circuiting

Each block is given two track circuits: one immediately inside the signal, which separately guards the overlap zone, and one, called the *berth* track circuit, which is specific to its block. Electrically this system is similar to double blocking, the output of the overlap-zone track circuit being added to that of the two adjacent berth track circuits by means of AND gates as shown in Figure 15.3.

Chapter 16: Capacitor discharge system for turnout motors

Most turnout motors consist of a pair of solenoids, both enclosing a common armature. A pulse of power, which may be AC or DC, is applied to one of the solenoids to draw the armature into it. A pulse of power is applied to the other solenoid to draw the armature back again. A spigot on the armature provides for its mechanical link to the turnout tiebar, or perhaps to the counterbalance of a semaphore signal.

The DC resistance of each solenoid is typically around 5 Ω, so with a typical power supply of about 16 V the current consumption will be about 3 A. Consequently considerable power is dissipated in turnout motors, which seem to delight in burning themselves out. To prevent this it is essential that power be applied for only a few moments — just long enough to allow the armature time to move. One favourite way to power turnout motors is capacitor charge or discharge. If the capacitor is large enough this can with very simple circuitry provide a suitably short burst of current.

Figure 16.1 shows a suitable circuit. In its simplest form it consists only of SPDT switch S1, capacitor C1, the two solenoids and a 22 V *smoothed* power supply. When S1 is set to the upper position, capacitor C1 charges up via solenoid L1. As long as the switch is kept in this position, the capacitor will be kept fully charged, which is useful. When the switch is moved to the *lower*

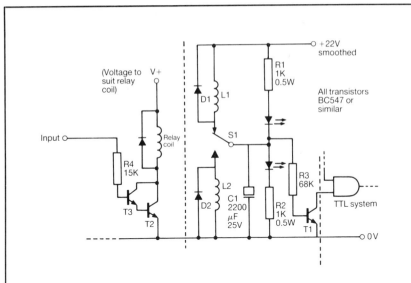

Figure 16.1 Capacitor charge/discharge system for turnout motors. The turnout motor solenoids are represented by L1 and L2. S1 may be a switch (SPDT) or relay contacts driven by the electronic circuitry to the left of the dotted line. R3/T1 provides a TTL-compatible output.

position, the capacitor discharges through solenoid L2 and, as long as the switch is kept in that position, the capacitor will be short-circuited and therefore kept discharged. A useful feature is that this eliminates the need for those awkward passing-contact switches. Any good-quality SPDT switch will do. For automatic operation, which we shall discuss later, the switch may be replaced by relay contacts. Another convenient feature of this circuit is that a digital indication of the setting of the turnout (or signal) can be obtained from the 'top' of the capacitor. When the capacitor is charged, the voltage will equal the supply voltage. When the capacitor is discharged, the voltage will be zero.

So, we can fit a pair of LEDs, shown in Figure 16.1, to indicate the setting of the turnout in a mimic diagram perhaps. If we want a TTL-compatible output, eg as an input to a junction signalling system (Chapter 18), it is essential to use a transistor as a 'buffer' between the 22 V 'high' and the TTL's 5 V 'high'. This, too, is shown in Figure 16.1. Note that when the switch is in the 'upper' position and the capacitor is charged, the output obtainable from the collector of the transistor will be a logical '0'.

The diodes D1 and D2 protect the electronic circuitry against the effects of inductive overshoot when the solenoids are de-energised. These diodes may be omitted if the basic circuit (no LEDs and no transistor) is being used.

Automatic operation

For automatic operation SPDT switch S1 is replaced by SPDT relay contacts and again any good quality relay will do. The contacts are never required to *break* current, which is the most demanding operation.

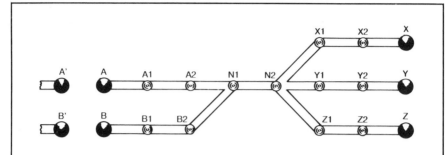

Figure 17.1 Part of a modern-image but freelance route setting panel. The black circles are drawstops; the smaller white circles are lamp bezels.

The relay may be driven by transistor circuitry such as that shown in Figure 16.1 and much depends on the rating of the relay coil, although you may not need a Darlington. The input of this circuit is TTL-compatible. A logical '1' applied to the input will energise the relay coil and use is made of this facility in the route-setting system described in Chapter 17.

Chapter 17: Route setting

In old-fashioned signal boxes (or 'towers' as they are called in North America) each turnout ('point' or 'switch') and each signal was operated by its own individual lever. As a train entered the area covered by the box, the signalman ('towerman') had to set up its route which might involve the operation of a dozen or so levers. On many model railways a similar practice was observed. In modern power boxes, however, the task is greatly simplified. A huge mimic diagram shows at once all that is happening in the area controlled. In order to set up a route the signalman has only to pull a drawstop for the starting point and another for the destination and the whole route is set up automatically, all the turnouts and signals being changed as necessary. The route set up is indicated on the mimic diagram by white lights and these are replaced by red lights as the train enters the area and activates its track circuits. The aspect of the signals is indicated in a simplified manner, a red lamp alongside the track representing a danger signal and a green lamp a signal showing any proceed aspect, which may be a yellow or double yellow.

Interest in modern practice is growing apace among railway modellers and several have satisfactorily installed this kind of route setting panel. Obviously each panel must be tailor-made for the layout or part of a layout that it represents, which means that only general guidance can be given here. It is assumed that track circuiting is installed throughout and that each turnout is controlled by the automatic turnout system described in Chapter 16. Only one route at a time can be set on the system to be described, but it is surprisingly simple.

Electronics of the panel

Figure 17.1 shows part of a route-setting control panel. Routes can be set from

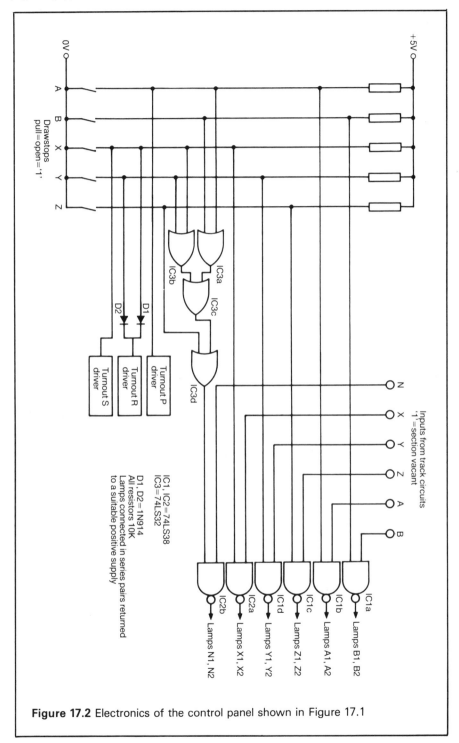

Figure 17.2 Electronics of the control panel shown in Figure 17.1

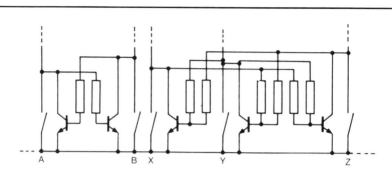

Figure 17.3 An optional protection circuit for the drawstops in Figures 17.1 and 17.2: all transistors BC547 or similar; all resistors 10K.

A or B via N to X, Y or Z. X, Y and Z may represent sidings. A and B may represent parts of a main line, A' and B' representing one end of the next section of that main line.

There are five drawstops that we shall consider: A, B, X, Y and Z. Each drawstop, when pulled, breaks a contact and allows a number of logic inputs to rise from logical '0' to '1'. Figure 17.2 shows the electronics behind the panel. The inputs from the drawstops and the relevant track circuits are applied to an array of NAND gates (IC1 and IC2). When a route is selected *and* its track circuit shows the line as available, a gate receives two '1's on its inputs and so its output goes to '0'. The ICs selected are the 7438 or 74LS38, each of which has standard inputs for its family, but the output section has higher current handling characteristics, so it can drive a few miniature lamps direct. The 7438 has open-collector outputs; the similar 7437 has push-pull output.

The central section of the route, N, has its lights illuminated if it is vacant and if *any* route is set. So the four OR gates (IC3) are used to combine the outputs from the five drawstops for application to IC2b. The three turnout drivers (see Chapter 16 for a suitable circuit) are driven direct from the drawstop contacts, turnout R via diode matrix, since it must be actuated for routes to X or Y. (We could use an OR gate, but two diodes are cheaper and the turnout driver, unlike TTL, will respond to positive-going inputs.)

An optional extra for the drawstops is shown in Figure 17.3. Unless you can find or fabricate mechanically linked drawstops, in which the pulling of one cancels the adjacent one (eg pulling B causes A to return), there is the danger of two conflicting routes being set simultaneously (eg A *and* B). We can eliminate this ambiguity quite simply by connecting an npn transistor across each pair of contacts and arranging that this receives bias when any conflicting route is set. So, if you pull A (B not being pulled), B's transistor is turned on (although for the time being it is of course short-circuited by the B drawstop contacts) and if you now inadvertently pull B, its transistor holds the circuit closed, so that route A remains set. The route set up will be displayed by the white lights on the panel, irrespective of the drawstops pulled.

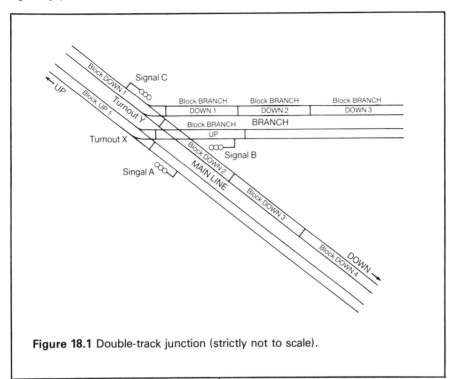

Figure 18.1 Double-track junction (strictly not to scale).

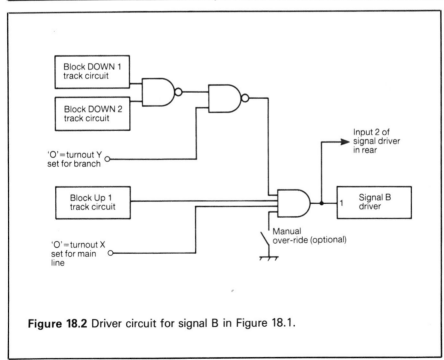

Figure 18.2 Driver circuit for signal B in Figure 18.1.

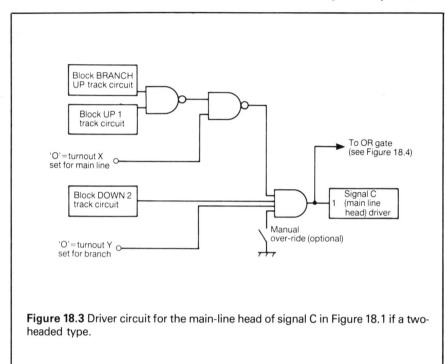

Figure 18.3 Driver circuit for the main-line head of signal C in Figure 18.1 if a two-headed type.

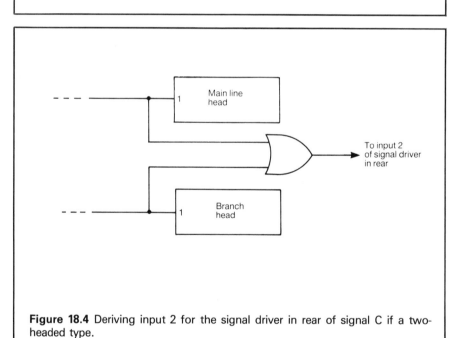

Figure 18.4 Deriving input 2 for the signal driver in rear of signal C if a two-headed type.

Chapter 18: Junction signalling

The signalling systems considered so far have all related primarily to *running signals,* ie signals guarding blocks without the complications of junctions. These signals, when functioning automatically, are operated simply by the movements of trains through the block sections. At junctions, however, the signals must also take into consideration the setting of the turnouts (formerly called 'points' in the UK and 'switches' in the USA). For this reason it is necessary to feed into any junction signalling system information about the setting of the turnouts. There are several ways in which electrical outputs for feeding into the signalling system may be derived:

1 Some turnouts, eg the long obsolete (but still obtainable) Hornby Dublo live-frog OO/HO types, incorporate built-in SPDT contacts linked mechanically to the turnout tiebar.

2 Peco manufactures a SPDT switch which may be fitted to the Peco turnout motor.

3 If the turnout is electrically operated by an electronic system, eg as in Chapter 16 of this book (or Project 22 in *Practical Electronics for Railway Modellers*), a suitable output can be obtained from the driver circuit.

4 Some passing-contact switches intended for the electric operation of turnout motors also include SPDT contacts from which a suitable output can be derived.

5 On some parts of my own layout I have tackled the problem the other way round. These turnouts are operated mechanically by a spring-and-cable mechanism from the toggles of a bank of drawstop-type switches whose electrical contacts provide the inputs to the signalling system.

6 If all else fails, it should not be beyond the ingenuity of the average model railway enthusiast to fashion some means of linking the turnout tiebar to a microswitch.

Junction signals are of two types; at a *trailing junction* lines converge and at a *facing junction* lines diverge, so the trains have a choice of routes. Some signals at facing junctions have a separate head for each route, while in others a single head shows the appropriate aspect for whichever route is set up, the route being identified by some sort of indicator. Any junction is, of course, both trailing and facing depending on the direction of a train approaching it. At a double-track running junction, one route will send the train across the path of oncoming traffic, which can add further complications.

Trailing junctions

Figure 18.1 shows a typical double-track junction. You will notice that there are two trailing-junction signals, A and B, and one facing junction signal, C, with the two trailing junction signals requiring quite different inputs. Signal A is simplest as all that is needed is a simple manual over-ride-type circuit; the type shown in Figure 13.3 is recommended. When turnout X is set for the branch, a '0' must be applied to one input of the AND gate, so that input 1 of the signal driver receives a '0' setting the signal to danger.

Signal B is more complicated. A similar over-ride to that on signal A must be incorporated, but this time, of course, it is when turnout X is set for the main line that a '0' must be applied to the AND gate. However, the crossing

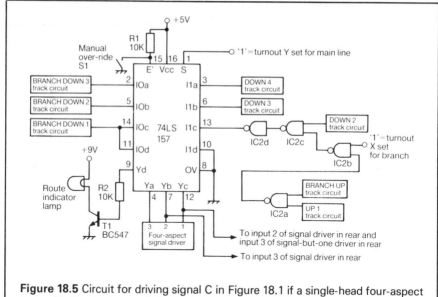

Figure 18.5 Circuit for driving signal C in Figure 18.1 if a single-head four-aspect type with 'feather' route indicator.

introduces further complications. Clearly we must also over-ride signal B to danger when turnout Y is set for the down main line and a train is approaching the junction or crossing it. Figure 18.2 shows a suitable scheme for feeding input 1 of signal B's driver. The drivers themselves for signals A and B may, of course, be any of the driver circuits described in Chapter 12.

Facing junctions

The facing junction signal C in Figure 18.1, as indicated earlier, could be either of two types. It could employ separate heads for the main line and the branch or it could use a single head with a route indicator. In the UK the commonest types of route indicator are the 'feather' of three or five 'lunar' lights illuminated when the line is cleared for a diverging route and the 'theatre'-type alphanumeric indicator which is separately treated in Chapter 20. Electrically, the two-headed version may be regarded as two separate signals, one for each route, the head for the unselected route being over-ridden to danger by the setting of turnout Y.

For the branch head the circuitry is simple, resembling that of signal A. All that is needed is a simple over-ride to set this head to danger when turnout Y is set for the main line. For the main-line head the circuitry is exactly like that for signal B. The head must be over-ridden to danger when turnout Y is set for the branch or when turnout X is set for the branch and there is a train on the up branch approaching the junction or crossing the junction. Thus, we end up with a circuit like that in Figure 18.3. Unfortunately our difficulties do not end here. If the signalling is three- or four-aspect, we need to set the signal in rear of C to yellow if *both* heads of C are at danger. To do this we need an OR gate or its equivalent as shown in Figure 18.4.

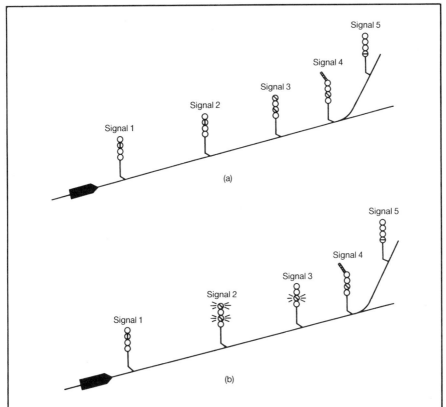

Figure 19.1 Four-aspect signalling on the approach to a running junction: **(a)** the 'traditional' system; **(b)** the system recently introduced on parts of British Rail—signals 2 and 3 show flashing yellow aspects.

If signal C is a single-head type with route indicator, life gets really interesting. To make sure that all eventualities are covered, let's assume the worst by making signal C a four-aspect type with a 'feather'-type route indicator. 'Feathers' are available in 4 mm scale in the 'EKCON' range of products from CCH Models and they are illuminated by a 'grain-of-rice' subminiature filament lamp which operates well from a 9 V supply. The difficulty is that the three inputs to the standard four-aspect signal driver (see Chapter 12) must all be simultaneously switched between the three main-line block track circuit outputs in advance (Down 2, Down 3 and Down 4) and the three branch line block track circuit outputs (Branch down 1, Branch down 2 and Branch down 3) in advance. This looks like a candidate for a three-pole, double-throw switch ganged to the turnout switch. However, although we could use a switch or a relay to perform this function, their use is not recommended for reasons of expense, convenience and reliability for all mechanical switches are prone to wear. The good news is that those responsible for the design of TTL have anticipated our problem and produced a 'chip' which seems to have this very application in mind: the 74157 (or the

74LS157). This is called a 'quad two-input data selector' or 'multiplexer'. It is, effectively, a four-pole two-way logic switch and it selects one set of four inputs out of two sets. (See Appendix 4 for more detailed information.)

Figure 18.5 shows the resulting circuit. Three of the four 'selects' in the '157 switch the inputs to the conventional four-aspect signal driver. Note that the Down 2 input includes the now familiar arrangements to over-ride the signal to danger if a train from the branch should be crossing its path. Only a two-input AND gate is needed and this is provided by a pair of NANDs which neatly uses all four gates on a 74LS00. One 'select' has been used to derive bias for a transistor switching the 'feather' route indicator. This correctly only illuminates the 'feather' when the turnout is set for the branch and the first block (at least) in the branch is available.

An interesting feature of the '157 is its 'enable' input (pin 15). As long as this is kept at '0', the device functions normally but if a '1' is applied to it, the four outputs all go to '0'. This provides us with a useful manual over-ride. If S1 is switched to the 'high' position, '0's will be applied to all inputs of the signal driver, setting it to danger, and the route indicator will be extinguished.

If signal C is a three-aspect signal, the same arrangements will apply, but one 'select' of the '157 will not be used.

Chapter 19: Flashing yellow aspects

The introduction of the Inter-City 125 high-speed trains (HSTs) on British Rail caused an interesting problem regarding junction signalling. HSTs have superior braking which enables the drivers to delay the application of the brakes. For example, the drivers learned by experience that they could pass a signal at double yellow and only apply the brakes on passing the next signal at yellow as there was still adequate braking distance.

Difficulties arose because in UK practice multiple-aspect signalling is also used to regulate the speed of trains approaching junctions. In Figure 19.1a the diverging route at the junction is speed restricted to, say, 40 mph. Standard practice to slow down trains taking this diverging route is to manually over-ride signal 5 to danger. When the turnout is set for the diverging route, therefore, signal 4 would display single yellow plus the diverging route indication, signal 3 would display double yellow and signals 2 and 1 green. As a train approaches signal 4, the manual over-ride on signal 5 is automatically removed, so that signals 5 and 4 change to less restrictive aspects. Now, there was a danger that HST drivers might ignore the double-yellow aspect of signal 3, believing that at signal 4 they would still have adequate braking distance, and approach signal 4 at 100mph, almost at once entering the diverging route dangerously above its 40 mph restriction. The problem was overcome by the introduction of two new aspects, which advise train drivers that they are routed for a restricted divergence and must adjust their speed accordingly. Manual over-ride is applied to signal 5 as before, and signal 4 shows single yellow plus divergence as before. Signal 3, however, shows a *flashing* single yellow aspect and signal 2 a flashing double-yellow aspect. Signal 1, as before, shows green. As before, when the train approaches signal 4, the manual over-ride is removed from signal 5. (This is shown in Figure 19.1b.) The flashing aspects flash at 70 cycles per minute (1.2 Hz), 50 per cent duty cycle. In the flashing double-yellow aspect, the aspects flash in unison, not alternately.

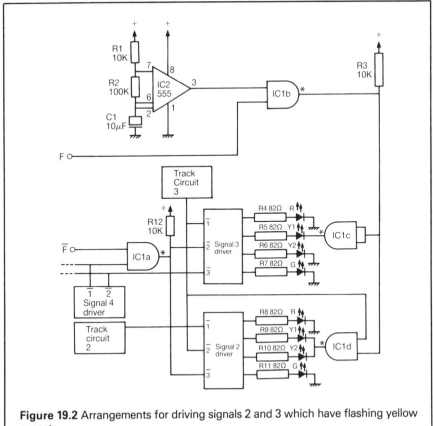

Figure 19.2 Arrangements for driving signals 2 and 3 which have flashing yellow aspects.

Modelling the system

If you are a modern-image modeller and if your layout is sufficiently large to justify four-aspect signalling, you can add interest and variety to your layout by modelling a flashing yellow-aspect system. Alternatively, you may be able to adapt the following to simulate the flashing yellow aspects seen on some continental railways. What follows is a description of one way of reproducing the British Rail system. We shall start by considering the signals in reverse numerical order.

Signal 5: Any four-aspect signal driver (Figures 12,7, 12.8 or 12.9) is suitable provided it is fitted with a manual over-ride (Chapter 13) whose free input is taken from $\overline{F}$ — I'll explain what this means later.

Signal 4: Any four-aspect signal driver with diverging route indicator and two-way input selector (Figure 18.5) is suitable.

Signal 3: This signal is required on occasions to display the flashing single yellow aspect. Only the signal driver circuit of Figure 12.7 is suitable and it must be connected as shown in Figure 19.2. A manual over-ride from $\overline{F}$ is applied via AND gate IC1a to *input 2*. When this is activated, the single yellow

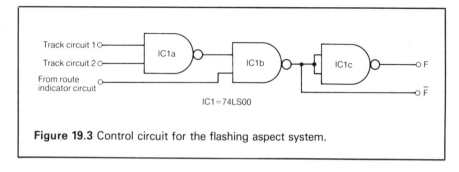

Figure 19.3 Control circuit for the flashing aspect system.

aspect is displayed (over-riding the double yellow or green aspects) unless, of course, input 1 is also activated whereupon the signal will go to danger.

The yellow 1 aspect is grounded via the output of open-collector AND gate IC1c, whose inputs are taken from the output of IC1b. One input of IC1b is fed from the output of IC2, a 555 timer set up as a free running multivibrator at 1.2 Hz and about 50 per cent duty cycle. The other input of IC1b is taken from input F (the inverse of input $\bar{F}$). We shall see shortly how inputs F and $\bar{F}$ are derived.

When the flashing system is on, a '1' from input F is applied to one input of IC1b and the pulses from the 555 are applied to the other. The output therefore consists of the pulses derived from the 555 and these are applied to IC1c which is used as an open-collector buffer. During the pulses the open-collector output transistor is off and so the yellow aspect's return current is interrupted. Between the pulses, the output transistor conducts, so current passes normally. Consequently aspect yellow 1 is made to flash at 1.2 Hz. An open-collector IC is used to preclude the possibility of reverse-polarity voltage being applied to the LED when the output of IC1c is high. When the flashing system is off, F is at '0', so a '0' is applied to one input of IC1b. This holds its output — and therefore that of IC1c — at '0', ie conductive, regardless of the pulses from the 555 which are still being applied to the other input. The yellow aspect may now be illuminated normally, ie without flashing.

Signal 2: This signal is required on occasion to display the flashing double-yellow aspect. It is driven in a manner generally similar to signal 3, as Figure 19.2 shows. Only the driver circuit of Figure 12.7 is suitable. The manual over-ride from IC1a's output is applied to input 3 of the signal driver to activate the double-yellow aspect. Both yellow aspects are returned through the output transistor of IC1d, so that the two aspects flash in unison when required.

You may wonder why there is also a feed from input 2 of signal 2's driver to IC1d. The reason is as follows. When a train passes signal 2 at flashing double yellow, signal 2 goes to danger and when, a little later, it passes signal 3 at flashing single yellow, signal 3 also goes to danger. No problem so far but soon the train leaves signal 2's track circuit, so signal 2 should now go to *normal* (ie non-flashing) single yellow. However, input F is still at '1', so we must use an independent system to over-ride IC1d into a continuous '0' output which will steadily sink the yellow aspect's current.

Signal 1: Signal 1 is not affected by the flashing system, so may be driven in the normal way. Any four-aspect driver circuit may be used.

Control

The flashing system is controlled as follows; the flashing system is on when a train is in section 1 (that is, the section guarded by signal 1 and approaching signal 2) *or* in section 2 (approaching 3) *and* the turnout is set for the diverging route, the first section (at least) of which is vacant, so that the 'feather' route indicator is illuminated. It helps if there is a long overlap beyond signal 3 so that it is not until the train is, prototypically, approaching signal 4 that it vacates section 2, clearing the system. The two complementary outputs F and F̄ are '1' and '0' respectively when the flashing system is on. Figure 19.3 shows the simplicity of the control circuit. Note the input from the route-indicator circuit; this is taken straight from the output of the fourth 'select' of the data selector on the input of signal 4's driver circuit (Figure 18.5). This input goes high when the route indicator is illuminated.

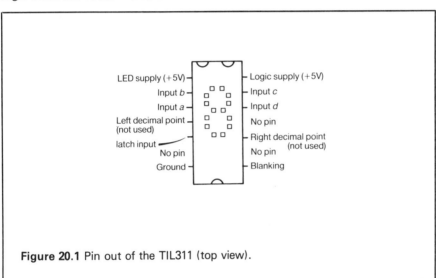

Figure 20.1 Pin out of the TIL311 (top view).

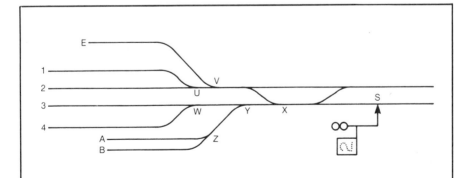

Figure 20.2 Example of a 'theatre' indicator on the approach to a terminus.

Chapter 20: 'Theatre' indicator

On the approach to a complex facing junction offering a variety of routes the signal is often accompanied by what is called a 'theatre'-type route indicator. This is an alphanumeric display composed of a matrix of lamps. When a route is set up and the signal is cleared, a number or letter is displayed by the theatre indicator to tell the train driver which route is set. This type of unit is often used on the approach to a terminus or other principal station and the character displayed is often the platform number into which the approaching train is being routed.

Seven-segment LED displays have sometimes been used to model 'theatre' indicators, but these pose a number of problems. Firstly, a seven-segment display simply does not look like a theatre indicator. Secondly, a seven-segment display simply needs complicated wiring and decoding. Both problems are solved, to some extent, by the use of the TIL311 unit.

The TIL311 is a hybrid device that contains an LED display composed of dots, not segments, and is, therefore, more prototypical in appearance. Moreover, it displays not only the numerals 0 to 9 but also the letters A to F, and it contains a TTL-compatible on-board decoder, which considerably simplifies the electrics. All you have to do is to feed into the unit a four-bit binary code for the required character. The TIL311 also includes a latching facility, although this is not of use in the application that we have in mind. There is a 'latch' pin to which a logical '0' must be applied as the binary input is fed in. If a '1' is applied to this input, the character being displayed will be held unchanged even if the binary input is changed. For our application this pin must be held at a logical '0'. Another facility of the TIL311 which is useful, and indeed essential for our application, is its blanking arrangement. If a logical '1' is applied to the blanking pin, the display is extinguished. You may be able to arrange for this pin to be connected to the input to the adjacent signal's red aspect, so that the display is blanked prototypically whenever the signal is at danger.

Hexadecimal binary input codes

d	c	b	a			d	c	b	a	
0	0	0	0	= 0		1	0	0	0	= 8
0	0	0	1	= 1		1	0	0	1	= 9
0	0	1	0	= 2		1	0	1	0	= A
0	0	1	1	= 3		1	0	1	1	= B
0	1	0	0	= 4		1	1	0	0	= C
0	1	0	1	= 5		1	1	0	1	= D
0	1	1	0	= 6		1	1	1	0	= E
0	1	1	1	= 7		1	1	1	1	= F

The unit also includes two decimal points, one in front and one behind the digit. But these are not of use in our application. Figure 20.1 gives the pin-out of the TIL311.

Needless to say, the TIL311 does have some drawbacks. There is a price to be paid for the convenience of the marriage in one package of both TTL and LED technologies. Literally a price has to be paid —of between £6 and £10 per unit. Another drawback is that the display is in red (no other colour being

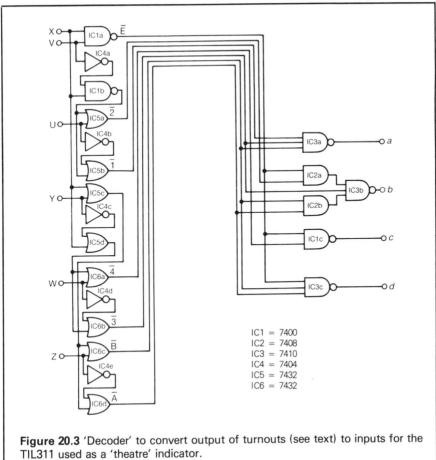

Figure 20.3 'Decoder' to convert output of turnouts (see text) to inputs for the TIL311 used as a 'theatre' indicator.

available) but the dots are so small and so bright that this is hardly noticeable. Also the unit is suitably sized for both 4 mm and 7 mm scale installations.

Example of its application

Figure 20.2 shows part of a layout, consisting of a station having four platforms numbered 1 to 4, two goods or parcels bays called A and B and a siding, which might be the approach to a motive power depot, designated E. When the signal S is cleared for one of these destinations, the appropriate character (1, 2, 3, 4, A, B or E) is illuminated in the theatre indicator. Although the figure shows the station as a terminus, the same arrangements would apply if it were one approach to a through station.

The problem is how do we convert the setting of the turnouts to the binary coded input needed by the TIL311? As with normal junction signalling, you *must* have some kind of electrical output from your turnouts which gives a digital, TTL-compatible indication of the turnout setting. (See Chapter 18 for a selection of methods of doing this.) For simplicity I have assumed that each turnout is fitted with a system that provides a logical '1' when it is set to the upper (E-wards) position and a logical '0' when set to the lower (B-wards) position. This only demands a single-pole, single-throw switch which 'makes' when the turnout is in the lower position.

We now need a 'decoder' to convert the inputs from the turnouts to binary coded inputs for the display. There are six turnouts and therefore $2^6 = 64$ possible combinations of turnout setting but, as there are only seven possible destinations, the system contains a lot of 'redundancy'. For example, when turnouts X and V are both in the upper position, the destination is E no matter what the setting of the other four turnouts. Thus, we can construct a 'Truth Table' for our decoder in which there will be many X (don't care) inputs.

Turnout output						Destination	Decoder output			
X	V	U	Y	W	Z	and display	d	c	b	a
1	1	X	X	X	X	E	1	1	1	0
1	0	1	X	X	X	1	0	0	0	1
1	0	0	X	X	X	2	0	0	1	0
0	X	X	1	1	X	3	0	0	1	1
0	X	X	1	0	X	4	0	1	0	0
0	X	X	0	X	1	A	1	0	1	0
0	X	X	0	X	0	B	1	0	1	1

From this Truth Table we can design our decoder and oddly enough we start at the back and design forwards.

The easiest way to deliver the positive logic outputs from a variety of input combinations is to use NAND gates to service the outputs. We 'normally' keep all the NAND gate inputs high so that the outputs are low. Now a '0' on any input will drive that gate's output high. Looking down the last four columns of the Truth Table shows us that a two-input gate will suffice for the *c* output line, three-input gates are needed for the *d* and *a* lines and we need *five* inputs on the gate for the *b* line. However, a five-input gate is not made, so we use up the spare three-input gate on the 7410 providing the *d* and *a* outputs and 'expand' its fan in with a pair of two-input AND gates. Now we read through the Truth Table a line at a time. For the E display we need to identify those situations when the X and V inputs are both high. So, we feed these two inputs to NAND gate IC1a (in Figure 20.3). When activated it delivers a '0' output which is fed to an input of each of the *d, c* and *b* output gates.

We can take the next two lines of the Truth Table together. We need to identify situations when X is high and V is low. So, we put the V input through an inverter (IC4a) and apply its output and the X input to NAND gate IC1b, but now we need to discover whether it is platform 1 or platform 2 that is routed. This depends on the setting of turnout U. Thus, we feed the output of IC1b to one gate each of OR gates IC5a and IC5b. We apply the U input to the other inputs of these gates, to IC5b via inverter IC4b. IC5a and IC5b therefore deliver '0' outputs when destinations 2 and 1 have been selected respectively. These outputs are fed to the appropriate output NAND gates.

All the remaining destinations (3, 4, A and B) depend on the X input being low and, also, on the input to Y. So, an input from X is applied to one gate each of OR gates IC5c and IC5d and the input from Y is applied to the other inputs of these gates, to IC5d via inverter IC4c.

The output of IC5d is a '0' when X is low and Y is high, the destination platforms 3 or 4, depending on the setting of turnout W. Therefore, the output of IC5d is applied to one input each of OR gates IC6a and IC6b; the output of W is fed to the other inputs, to IC6b via inverter IC4d. Thus, IC6a gives a '0' output when a route is set to platform 4 and IC6b gives a '0' output when platform 3 is the destination. These outputs are fed to the appropriate output NAND gate inputs.

The output of IC5c is a '0' when X is low and Y is low, the destination being the bays A or B, depending on the setting of turnout Z. The output of IC5c is applied to one input each of OR gates IC6c and IC6d and the output of Z is fed to the other inputs, to IC6d via inverter IC4e. Thus, IC6c gives a '0' output when a route is set to bay B and IC6d when a route is set to bay A. These outputs are fed to the appropriate output NAND gates.

You can work it out for yourself if you wish: the decoder really does convert the turnout settings to the binary coding for the selected destination and this will be displayed by the TIL311, providing it is not blanked out.

The circuit exactly as described only works for the layout shown in Figure 20.2 but the principles are the same for any situation. With a little practice, and a little of the ingenuity for which railway modellers are renowned, the circuitry for a 'theatre' indicator for almost any situation can be deduced.

Part 5

Automatic train control projects

In this section a varied assortment of circuits are gathered together which all, in some way, control the train — or, at least, relieve the operator of some of the more tedious aspects of train control.

The first two are 'passive' in that they need no power supply of their own. Chapter 21 describes a circuit which enables a train to run round a reversing loop without stopping, while Chapter 22 is about a unit which provides gentle slowdowns and stops, but cannot restart a train.

Chapter 23 describes an interlock to stop trains automatically at danger signals and restart them when the signal clears with Chapter 24 extending this idea to timed station stops. In both of these projects it is assumed that the 'autostop' unit of 6 is fitted to the controller in use. The last two Chapters in this section are devoted to that age-old quest of railway modellers — multiple train control — but both avoid the complications of 'command control' systems, eg the need for 'modules' in the locos. Chapter 25 considers the idea of giving every section its own controller, a scheme that is not as bizarre as it sounds. Chapter 26 takes the idea a stage further — progressive cab control is neither as complicated nor as expensive as it sounds and permits different trains to run successively over the same section, each powered by a different controller, without operator intervention. The system does the 'thinking' and 'switching' and will even bring a train to a gentle halt when it reckons it's on a collision course.

Chapter 21: Automatic reversing loop

Reversing loops have always caused difficulties on two-rail model railways. The problem is, as Figure 21.1 shows, that the outer rail of the loop is continuous with the live rail at one end of the loop and with the return rail at the other end, causing a permanent short circuit. Standard practice has been to isolate a length of the outer rail in the loop and to arrange for it to be switched to the live or return side of the power circuit as necessary.* As a train runs around the loop, it must be stopped in the isolated section and, while it is

*The standard reference books on model railway electrification say that it is necessary to isolate and switch the inner rail of the loop as well. In fact this is only necessary if the turnout used is a live-frog type. If it is an insulated-frog type, the turnout action itself will correctly switch the supply to the inner rail of the loop.

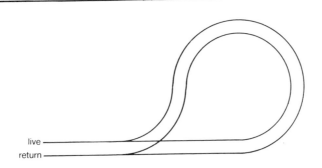

Figure 21.1 Simplified drawing of a reverse loop. Note that the outer rail of the loop is continuous with the live rail at one end and the return rail at the other, causing a permanent short circuit.

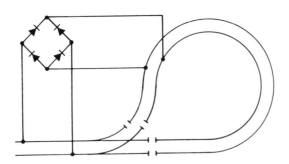

Figure 21.2 Automatic reversing loop with connections for clockwise running.

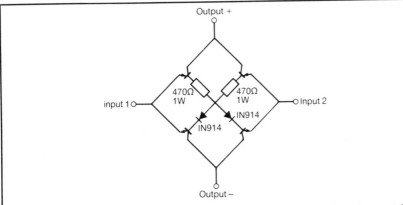

Figure 21.3 Transistor bridge rectifier. The transistors need to be matched complementary power types.

stopped, the polarity of the section is changed, the turnout is reset and the direction-change switch on the controller is operated. The train can now resume its journey round the loop and back on to the main line, where it is now running, of course, in the opposite direction. This stopping of the train and the three switching operations are clearly inelegant, although whatever improvements may be possible in convenience, it is inevitable that the turnout is changed and the direction switch operated while the train is in the loop. It is possible and, indeed, quite simple to arrange for trains to run around the loop *without stopping*. To do this it is necessary to isolate as much as possible of both outer and inner rails in the loop. Their power supply is derived from that of the main line via a bridge rectifier, as shown in Figure 21.2. You must decide whether you want your trains to run clockwise or anti-clockwise around the loop, since this depends upon the polarity of the connections to the bridge rectifier output (Figure 21.2 shows connections for clockwise running) and if you wish to vary the direction of running in the loop, you must fit a reversing switch between the bridge and the loop. The procedure now is to run the train into the loop (ensuring that the turnout is correctly set, of course) and, at any time while the train is wholly in the loop, change the turnout and the direction setting on the controller. It is not necessary to stop the train unless your controller has a combined speed and direction control like the one described in Chapter 5.

However, there is one disadvantage in the system just described, which is a property of the characteristics of the bridge rectifier. The voltage drop across this is about 2 V, and sufficient to cause a noticeable loss of speed as a train enters the loop. If this is unacceptable, consider replacing the bridge rectifier with the arrangement shown in Figure 21.3. This 'transistor bridge rectifier' behaves like its diode counterpart but has a much lower voltage drop of about 0.4 V total. This is because the voltage drop across a saturated transistor is rather less than that across a forward-biased diode. The circuit is more expensive, of course, since it demands four power transistors — but then in this life there is always a price to pay for any improvement in performance!

Chapter 22: 'Autoslow'

Project 3 in *Practical Electronics for Railway Modellers* described a capacitor slow-down unit for siding ends. As a loco approaches the end of a siding, it crosses a rail break, whereafter its supply is via a high-value electrolytic capacitor. As this charges up, its charge current — which is the loco's traction current — falls, giving a gradual slow-down. The trouble is that the effectiveness of this circuit varies widely according to the locomotive's characteristics. With a small light loco, such as the Mainline J72, the effect is impressive, whereas with my elderly Hornby Dublo 8F, which draws 1A, the charge-up is almost instantaneous and the slow-down unprototypically abrupt.

The 'autoslow' unit was designed as an improved version of my earlier capacitor slow-down system and in it the rate of slow-down is independent of the loco type and, usefully, adjustable. The device is 'passive', that is to say, it does not need an external power supply as it draws its power from the track.

How it works

Here it is necessary to refer to the circuit diagram in Figure 22.1. As a train

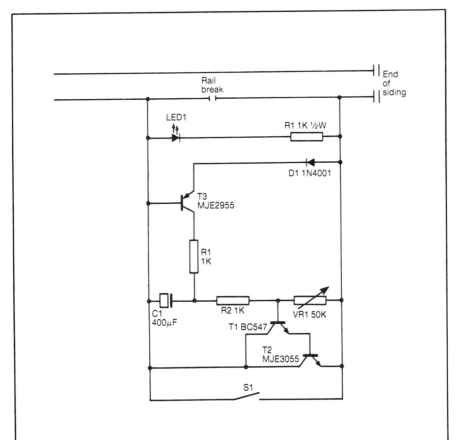

Figure 22.1 'Autoslow' unit: the rail break is in the rail which is positive when the train is going in the direction in which it is to be slowed.

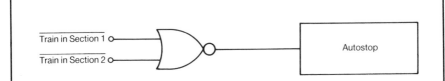

Figure 23.1 A simple interlock. It would not be satisfactory for reasons given in the text.

approaching the siding end crosses the rail break X its power feed is diverted via Darlington pair T1/T2. The train now completes the charge-up circuit for C1, which also includes R3, VR1 and the base/emitter junctions of the Darlington. The proportion of the charge-up time during which the Darlington conducts depends on the setting of VR1. With the components shown the slow-down time is adjustable from zero to about 10 seconds.

At first, C1's charge current is high, biasing the Darlington into saturation, so that there is little effect on the speed of the train. As the charge rises, the Darlington's bias current and, therefore, its collector current falls, slowing the train until eventually it stops. As the voltage across the Darlington rises, LED1 lights up and even after the train stops remains illuminated as long as the controller remains set 'into the siding'. Therefore the LED provides a useful 'train stopped but power still on' indication which is extinguished as soon as the controller is turned to stop or to the 'out of siding' direction (or if the train is removed from the siding).

Although this unit gives gentle *stops,* it cannot by itself give a gentle *start* (if you want automatic stops *and* starts, you need the 'auto*stop*' unit described in Chapter 6. As soon as the controller is set for the 'out of siding' direction, the power circuit is completed via D1 and T3's base/emitter junction and the train will give a normal controlled start, except that it will be subjected to two 'diode drops' across the two junctions (about 1.5 V). Transistor T3 now conducts removing any remaining charge on C1.

Optional switch S1 provides another interesting possibility for this unit as it may be used to give automatic gentle station stops in a through station. S1 is normally left open so that the unit functions in the normal way. To restart the train (in the same direction) *first* set the controller to 'stop', then close S1 so the train can now be started manually in the normal way. C1 will gradually discharge via VR1 and R2, but there will be no indication from LED1 and S1 must be reopened before the unit can stop another train. If it is left closed, trains will run through the station without stopping.

Chapter 23: Active interlock

Within this book, as in *Practical Electronics for Railway Modellers,* an 'active interlock' is a system which automatically causes a train to gradually slow down and stop as it approaches a signal at danger and to gently restart when the signal clears. There are many ways in which this could be achieved, but nearly all present savage complications. For instance, we could use a simple logic circuit like the one in Figure 23.1. This circuit activates the 'autostop unit' (Chapter 6) when there is a train in block 1 *and* in block 2. So, undoubtedly, it *would* activate the autostop unit when a train enters the block approaching a signal at danger guarding the next block in advance which is also occupied.

There are many other circumstances in which adjacent track circuits are simultaneously activated. For example, when a train passes from one block to the next, for a short while, both track circuits are activated. If you use overlap (Chapter 15), this 'short while' may well last several seconds — long enough to stop the train. We could build a timing circuit (Chapter 24) to delay the activation of the autostop system in order to allow for long overlaps.

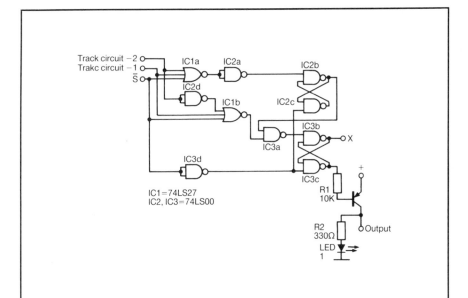

Figure 23.2 'Sequence controlled' interlock. Output X is used in the timed station stop application (Chapter 24).

There are still other occasions when trains may legitimately occupy adjacent blocks. For example, on a single-track line, train 1 may be in a passing loop and train 2 passing it on the main line and proceeding on to the block in rear of train 1. The system in Figure 23.1 cannot distinguish between approaching trains and trains drawing apart. Clearly an efficient interlock system must do so. Hence the system described in this Chapter.

How it works

The circuit shown in Figure 23.2 is 'sequence controlled'. It needs three inputs: (i) input S is taken from input 1 of the driver circuit of the signal being interlocked, so that the system 'knows' when this signal is at danger; (ii) from the track circuit of the block (called block -1) on the approach to the interlocked signal, ie in rear of it and (iii) from the track circuit on the block (called block -2) in rear of block -1. All these inputs are negative true, ie activated by a logical '0'.

The interlock unit is activated by the passage of a train from block -2 to block -1 while the signal is at danger. When the train passes from block -2 to block -1, for a few moments (at least) both track circuits are activated simultaneously. If, at the same time, the signal is at danger IC1a receives three '0' inputs and delivers a '1' output, inverted back to '0' by IC2a. This sets the bistable IC2b/IC2c to what we call the 'standby' condition. As the train approaches the signal, it clears block -2 and activates only the track circuit for block -1. Now, NOR gate IC1b, which receives the same inputs as IC1a except that the output from track circuit -2 is inverted by IC3a, delivers a '1' output. The first bistable is now in its 'standby' condition and thus IC2d receives '1's on *both* inputs and delivers a '0' output, which sets a second bistable, IC3c/IC3d, to what we call the *activated* state. Output from this bistable, when activated, drives the interlock output. The two bistables can only be reset by the clearing of the signal. When the S input goes to '1', inverter IC3d converts this to a '0' which is fed to the reset inputs of both bistables.

If your controller has positive-going output before its reversing switch (as in Chapters 1, 2 and 3), you can connect the interlock output direct to the controller's autostop remote input. Otherwise, you will need the interface unit shown in Figure 6.3.

Although ths interlock comes into operation at the right moment and clears when it should do, it nevertheless poses one problem. If two or more controllers are in use on the layout (and presumably there are if an interlock is needed), how does the interlock unit know which controller's autostop unit to activate? The answer is that, as described, it does not but there are a number of ways in which it can make itself useful. These are as follows:

(i) If you are using cab control, you could arrange for an additional pole of each section's controller selector switch to be used to connect the interlock's output to the appropriate controller's autostop input.

(ii) If you use 'block section control' (Chapter 25), there is no problem. Each block section has its own controller, so there is no ambiguity.

(iii) If neither (i) nor (ii) is applicable, the following may be helpful. Using blocking diodes arrange for *every* interlock output to activate *every* controller's autostop unit. It may be useful if you can arrange for an alarm to sound as well. Put an LED in the output circuit of each interlock unit, so that you can see at a glance *which* interlock is operating. Then set the autostop switches on the other controllers to the 'Cancel' position to allow the other trains to proceed. (Remember to restore these switches to 'Remote' when the interlock clears.)

If you are considering the use of progressive cab control (Chapter 26), the system described in this book incorporates a comprehensive interlock system that 'knows' which controller's autostop input to address, so, the system described in this Chapter is not needed.

Problems

This circuit poses a number of problems for the unwary. It uses bistable latches which, in close proximity to a working model railway, may be subject to spurious setting and resetting as a consequence of electrical interference from the trains. If you find yourself in such difficulties try the following modifications individually or in any combination:

(i) Replace the '00s with '132s, which are pin-for-pin equivalents, but have harsher switching characteristics;

(ii) Connect a massive (470μF) electrolytic capacitor between the positive and negative supply lines *on the circuit board;*

(iii) Connect 0.1μF capacitors between all inputs and the supply negative rail.

Chapter 24: Automatic station stops

Chapter 23 showed how we can arrange for trains to stop automatically (but

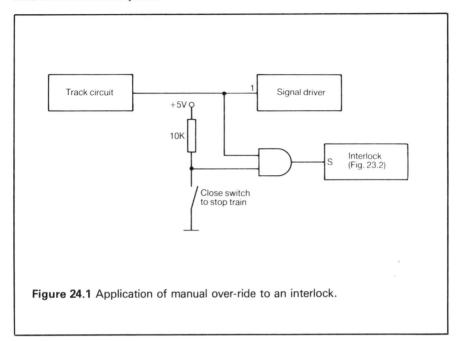

Figure 24.1 Application of manual over-ride to an interlock.

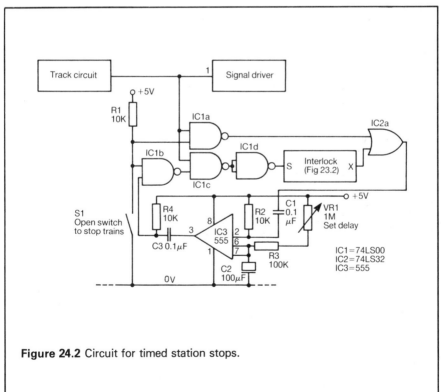

Figure 24.2 Circuit for timed station stops.

gradually) at danger signals and to restart automatically (and again gradually) when the signal clears. This Chapter extends that facility to stop trains automatically at stations for a timed period.

Often there is a signal (at one time known in UK practice as the starter signal) at the locomotive end of each platform of a through station. We shall assume the presence of this signal at the station where we want our train to stop automatically. If to this signal we were to apply the active interlock considered in Chapter 23 and the manual over-ride considered in Chapter 13, by over-riding the signal to danger, we could make the train stop automatically in the station. Releasing the manual over-ride would clear the signal and allow the train to restart. However, that would not be prototype practice. The aspect of the signal should not depend (at least not normally) on the intention of the railway to stop the train in the station; normally, it should depend only on the availability of the road in advance of the train. What we can do, however, is to apply a separate manual over-ride to input S of the interlock unit via an AND gate, as shown in Figure 24.1. Closing the switch will not affect the signal aspect — if clear, it will remain clear — but the interlock will now behave as though the signal were at danger and will stop the train in the station. Opening the switch will allow the train to proceed. Leaving the switch open will allow trains to pass through the station without stopping, providing of course that the signal is clear. If the signal is at danger, the train will be stopped by the interlock until the signal clears.

Timed station stops

The arrangement described above is not *fully* automatic. It stops the train in the station well enough, but you have to operate a switch to clear the interlock and restart the train. With a little more technology, however, we can arrange for the train to restart automatically after a timed interval.

The timing is carried out by the 555 timer IC which we met in Chapter 3. Again it is used as an interval timer, but this time the period timed is much longer. With the component values shown in Figure 24.2 the period is (approximately) 10 to 100 seconds. This period, incidentally, is the time from the *activation* of the interlock, when the train begins to slow down, until the *release* of the interlock, when the train will restart. In setting the delay, you must allow for the 'autostop' inertia time; the difference will represent the length of the station stop. For this application switch S1 must be *open* if automatic station stops are required. When this switch is open and when the signal is clear, input S of the interlock is activated bringing the interlock into action as a train enters the station and approaches the signal. As the interlock comes into action, a negative-going pulse is applied via C1 to the trigger input of the timer, which starts its timing cycle. During this timed period the interlock remains 'engaged' so that the train slows and stops. At the end of the timed period, the output of the timer goes 'low' and a negative-going pulse is applied via C3 to IC1b, where it causes a positive-going pulse of output which is applied via IC1c and IC1d (together acting as an AND gate) to input S of the interlock. This momentary '1' on input S resets the two bistables in the interlock, so that it clears and permits the train to restart. It is also ready immediately to stop the next train that approaches the signal.

If, at any stage during the timing cycle, switch S1 is closed, the interlock will clear and the train will restart. If the switch is left closed, trains will run through the station without stopping, provided, of course, that the signal is clear. If at any time the signal goes to danger, the interlock will be activated by an approaching train, whatever the setting of the switch, and the train will be stopped until the signal clears. If this should happen during the timer's cycle, the timed period will not be affected but the ending of the period will not release the interlock. The interlock will remain engaged until the signal clears. In this way the system retains full security and follows prototype practice.

Note that this circuit, like the interlock itself in Chapter 24, is liable to be affected by electrical interference from the trains. Ensure that there is a decoupling capacitor (100µF at least) between the positive and negative supply lines; if still troubled try 0.1µF capacitors between inputs and supply negative.

Chapter 25: Block section control

The philosopher's stone, as far as railway modellers are concerned, is a system enabling the independent control of a number of trains on the same layout. Recently a number of 'command control' systems have appeared on the market which meet this need.

These systems work by making the track permanently live and by using a 'module' inside each locomotive which is, in effect, a controller. This controller responds to 'commands' superimposed on the traction power by the master control unit. Some systems use pulse position modulation and others a 'radio-type' carrier frequency system to ensure that individual 'modules' respond only to those unique signals intended for them. Yet, 'command control' does pose certain problems, which is why no detailed description of such a system is included in this book. One reason for this is its sheer complication and expense. Another, more immediately practical problem, is *compatibility* for a loco cannot be run on a 'command-controlled' layout unless it has been fitted with the appropriate 'module'. So, your friend cannot run his newly acquired loco on your layout unless you temporarily fit a spare 'module'. Furthermore, the 'modules' occupy precious on-loco space, so it can be difficult, or even impossible, to fit them in smaller OO/HO locos. Command control for this reason is not at present practical for gauges smaller than HO.

If you do decide to change to command control, you must modify your entire layout all at once. You cannot do it by stages and the best results, I am reliably informed, are obtained from purpose-built layouts designed with command control in mind.

An alternative approach

There are, however, alternative approaches to multiple train operation, some of which overcome the problems associated with command control. Two such approaches are considered in this book: block section control and progressive cab control (Chapter 26). Both simulate prototype practice by dividing the layout into block sections, in each of which normally no more than one train is allowed at one time. In block section control each section has its own controller, dedicated to that block whereas in progressive cab control only a limited number of controllers are used as a vacant section is not connected to any controller, but when a train arrives its section is automatically connected to the same controller that the train had in the previous section.

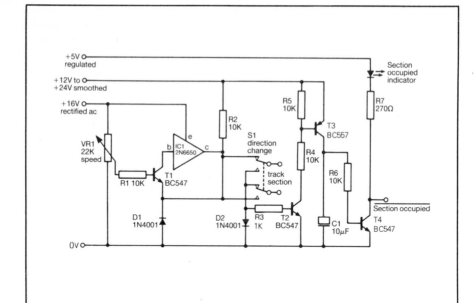

Figure 25.1 Combined controller/track circuit for one section of a block section control system.

Economically there is not much to choose between these. For a comparable layout, block section control will cost £*n* for output transistors (for all the controllers) while progressive cab control will cost £*n*/3 in output transistors, £*n*/3 in TTL ICs and £*n*/3 in relays. 'You pays your money and you takes your choice.'

Block section control

I must confess at this stage that I have not built block section control, nor do I know anyone else who has done so, but it was an option that I seriously considered. Only as a result of certain considerations did I opt for progressive cab control, but I am happy to share with you the thoughts that I had about block section control.

Let us imagine that you have a layout divided into 10 block sections. You will now need 10 of everything. In fact, what you have is virtually 10 layouts, end to end, so that trains can run between them. In view of this you will probably want the simplest of everything, initially at least, (not that this involves any compromise of quality or interest). Each block section needs a controller. The ideal types are those described in Chapters 1 and 3 and you should be able to make several in an evening although you might find the one in Chapter 3 preferable because heat sinks (which are bulky and expensive) are not needed.

Each block section may have its own track circuit unit. Since each section has its own controller, and therefore its own reversing switch, further economies can be made here by using a unidirectional track circuit unit *before* the reversing switch. The return-rail circuit of Chapter 10 is preferable, with a DPDT switch to the two rails of the section. (See Figure 25.1). Uniquely, using this system all your controllers may share the same unsmoothed power supply and all the track circuits the same smoothed supply, which may be derived from the unsmoothed controller supply.

If you install a signalling system, this too may be run from the track circuit smoothed supply via a 7805 or similar 5 V regulator IC. Interlocks (Chapter 23) are especially easy to add since there is no ambiguity as to which controller is addressed, but you will need to give each controller (or at least each interlocked controller) an 'autostop' unit (Chapter 6). Obviously you must ensure that your transformer can deliver all the power that the system will need. With, say, 10 sections you may have as many as five trains running simultaneously, plus peripheral systems (signalling etc) in action, too.

Operating the system

To operate the system you have to cultivate a 'block' mentality rather a 'cab' mentality. In other words, you must think like an old-style signalman rather than like a train driver. You have an array of controllers in front of you, but they relate to sections, not to trains, and the trains keep moving from block to block in a most disconcerting manner. For instance, suppose you want to stop a train at a station in certain block. Before the train enters the block you must set the speed control and direction switch as appropriate for that train when it enters the block. (The skill in operating block section control is to keep the train speed steady as trains pass from block to block, which is to say, from controller to controller.) You will see when the train enters the block by the illumination of the track circuit LED. As soon as the track circuit LED for the train's *previous* block is extinguished, your block has 'captured' the train and you can begin to reduce speed for the station stop. The situation to avoid is reversing a train into a block whose controller is set for forwards movement or *vice versa*. That causes very nasty short circuits.

Try to keep at least one vacant block between trains. So, if you have n sections, the maximum realistic number of trains in 'steam' is $n/2$. Even so, every train is going to be checked by signals at caution unless you reduce your traffic density to $n/3$. This system is ideally suited to automatic and semi-automatic operation making use of interlocks (Chapter 23) and timed station stops (Chapter 24). Once you've started a train on its journey, provided you set all the controllers to the appropriate speeds, you can leave your train to pursue its journey. You can leave the interlocks to stop it if it catches up with the train in front or to stop the train at some wayside station.

You may be different from me, but I find there's something therapeutic in just sitting back and watching the trains go by.

Chapter 26: Progressive cab control

Progressive cab control (PCC) is an alternative approach to multiple train operation. Unlike block section control (Chapter 25) trains keep their own controllers throughout their journey. It is less expensive than command control and offers the advantage that locos need no modification. Also conventional wiring is maintained, so you can install PCC step by step as time and money permit. Track circuiting (or some other reliable train detection system which gives an indication of block occupancy) is not only possible but an essential prerequisite.

PCC is based on 'cab control', a popular conventional system of model railway electrification. In cab control the layout is divided into control zones, each of which may be connected to any of several controllers by means of switches on the control panel. As the trains move from zone to zone, the operators throw the switches so that each train always keeps the same controller (or 'cab'). In PCC the principles are the same, but the switching is automatic, so that as a train enters a zone, that zone is automatically connected to the same controller the train had used in the previous zone.

It has been asserted that each PCC system must be tailor-made for its particular layout. This is true, of course, since it will inevitably depend on the number of zones or sections, the positions of the junctions and termini etc. as well as on the secondary functions that the system is required to serve. It is possible, however, to adopt a *modular* approach, each zone or section being serviced by an essentially similar unit. The number of units required and the way in which they are inter-connected will depend on the nature of the layout.

The unit described in this Chapter is very versatile, offering an interesting range of facilities, including a sophisticated interlock system. The 'standard' unit is for two-controller operation only, but the circuit for a three-controller version is also given. Units for use with any number of controllers can be deduced, but the complexity of the units increases dramatically as the number of controllers is raised. For most purposes the two- and three-controller versions are adequate, as will be seen later.

Prerequisites

To use the complete PCC system described in this Chapter, a number of conditions must be met. Various simplifications are possible and are discussed briefly later on. These may lead to the waiving of some of these prerequisites.

Firstly, your layout must be divided into cab control sections by rail breaks in the live rail and, secondly, your layout must be track-circuited or fitted with some other system for indicating the presence of trains in block sections. For convenience, this system will be called 'track circuiting' throughout this Chapter. Each track circuit must give a TTL-compatible logical '0' when its block is occupied. It simplifies matters if your cab control sections correspond to your track circuit sections, so you have one track circuit per cab control section. If you have more the track circuit outputs must be paralleled using AND gates (see Chapter 15). Track circuits may be live-rail or return-rail and may overlap (Chapter 15) if you wish. Thirdly, all controllers used must have their own fully independent power supplies. Also they must have positive-going output before the reversing switch (or relay contacts) and should be fitted with the 'autostop' facility described in Chapter 5. (The full-feature controller described in Appendix 1 is ideally suited for use with this PCC system.) Fourthly, there is an extra feature that must be fitted to controllers for use with this PCC system. This is an additional output terminal that is negative-going whenever the controller is set to reverse. There are several ways in which this may be provided. If the controller uses a reversing switch or relay having spare contacts, choose a pair of contacts that 'make' when reverse is selected, wire one to the controller's negative supply line and the other to the new output. If the controller uses a reversing relay and spare contacts are *not* available, insert an additional npn transistor with its emitter grounded to the supply negative line and its collector to the new socket. Arrange for it to receive base bias only when reverse is selected and resist the temptation to wire the output direct to any existing point in the circuit that happens to go negative when reverse is selected.

Note that this circuit, like that in Chapter 23, depends on bistable latches and is liable to interference from the trains. See the notes at the end of that chapter, which apply equally to this.

Function of the unit

Each unit (we are considering the two-controller version) has a front panel with three controls and six indicator LEDS. The controls are an SPDT 'isolate' switch and two push-button (push-to-make) switches labelled 'advise A' and 'advise B'. (A and B are the two controllers.) The six LEDs are labelled 'section isolated', 'unconnected train', 'A connected', 'B connected', 'A autostop' and 'B autostop'. Normally the unit will be used in conjunction with other similar units and you will have an array of these front panels as a part of your control console.

The unit also has no fewer than 19 connections, as follows:

  1 Supply positive (+ 5 V DC, smoothed, regulated).
  2 Supply negative and layout common return.
  3 Input from this section's track circuit ('0' = 'section occupied').
  4 'Section unavailable' output (to adjacent units).
  5 'Advise A' input (from all adjacent units).
  6 'Advise B' input (from all adjacent units).
  7 Selected controller live output to track (via track circuit if live-rail type).
  8 'Previous section unavailable' input (from previous section's unit).
  9 'Advise A' output (to previous section's unit).
  10 'Advise B' output (to previous section's unit).
  11 'Next section unavailable' input (from next section's unit).
  12 'Advise A' output (to next section's unit).
  13 'Advise B' output (to next section's unit).
  15 Reverse selected input (from controller A).
  16 Output to 'autostop' (of controller A).
  17 Live output of controller B.
  18 Reverse selected input (from controller B).
  19 Output to 'autostop' (of controller B).

(Throughout this Chapter *the next section* refers to the new section entered by a train travelling *forwards* and *the previous section* to the next section entered by a train travelling in *reverse*.)

As a train approaches the section under consideration, the unit for the section which the train currently occupies applies a logical '0' to our unit's 'advise A' or 'advise B' input. This 'advises' our section's unit that a train is approaching and tells it which controller is in use. Our unit, however, takes no further action until the train arrives in its section, whereupon it automatically connects the section to the controller that has been 'advised' (unless the section is isolated). The 'A connected' or 'B connected' LED lights up as appropriate.

The unit 'knows' whether or not the connected controller is set for reverse, so it now activates the appropriate 'advise' input of the unit for the section which the train will enter next. We'll look at the complications caused by

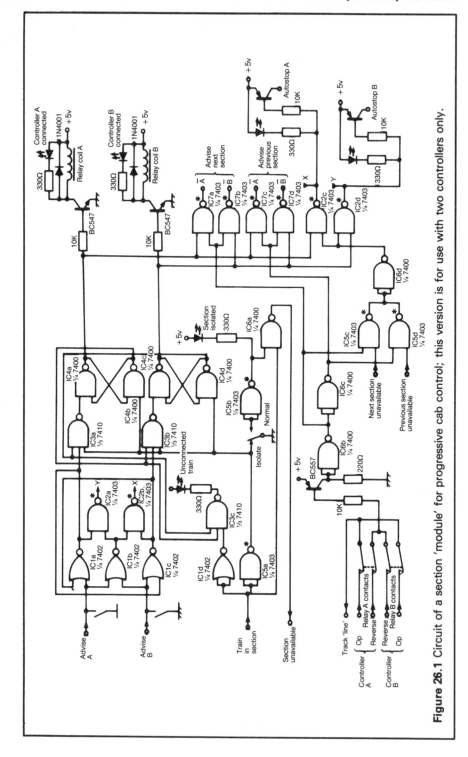

Figure 26.1 Circuit of a section 'module' for progressive cab control; this version is for use with two controllers only.

termini and junctions later. If, however, the destination section is occupied or isolated, the unit will activate the 'autostop' circuit of the connected controller and will light the appropriate 'autostop' LED. The 'autostop inertia' control on each controller should be set so that a train stops in just under an average section length. When the train leaves the section, the controller is disconnected. Under this system a controller cannot be connected to a vacant section.

The 'isolate' switch may be operated at any time. When the switch is thrown to the 'isolated' position any controller attached to the section is disconnected. While the switch remains in the 'isolated' position, no controller can be connected to the section and the 'section isolated' LED is illuminated.

Under certain circumstances a train may enter the section without the 'advise' input being activated, for example, at the start of an operating session, or if a train has been in the section while it was isolated but the switch is now restored to 'normal', or if a train is placed in the section by hand or is in a normally isolated siding now switched into the section. In any of these circumstances as well as whenever a train is isolated in the section, the 'unconnected train' LED will light. Under these circumstances the unit will not connect the section to either controller, for the simple reason that it does not 'know' which controller to connect. The 'advise A' or 'advise B' button must be pressed momentarily to enable the unit to connect the desired controller.

It is possible to change a train from one controller to another while in a section.* The train must be stopped and the 'isolate' switch operated for a moment and then restored to normal. The appropriate 'advise' button is now pressed for a moment to connect the selected controller. A unit cannot be 'advised' of more than one controller at a time. For example, if a unit is being advised of controller A on an approaching train, a subsequent '0' on the 'advise B' input will not change the 'advice' 'seen' by the unit. The unit will, however, interpret this as a hazard situation with trains on a collision course and will activate the 'autostop' system on controller B to bring that train to a halt. The train on controller A will be allowed to proceed. When the train on controller A has cleared the section, that on controller B will be 'released' and allowed into the section. Normally,† a unit cannot connect more than one controller to the same section (which would cause spectacular results), but the same controller may be connected to several sections, provided that each contains a train.

Description of the unit

Figure 26.1 gives the circuit diagram for the two-controller version. Readers without experience of TTL should refer to Appendix 4 for an introduction.

(i) Controller selection circuit. The 'advise' input (a logical '0') is applied to one of the two NOR gates, IC1a and IC1c. The function of these gates in their 'near bistable' configuration is to accept only the first input applied, if two inputs should be applied simultaneously, since the output of each gate inhibits

---

*There is a way in which a train can be switched from one controller to another at the border between sections without stopping the train. This will be considered later.

†At the start of an operating session, when the unit's power supply is first switched on, there is a possibility that the bistables controlling the relay drive circuitry may both latch in the 'engaged' state. If so, both 'A connected' and 'B connected' LEDS will light. The system *must* be cleared using the 'isolate' switch.

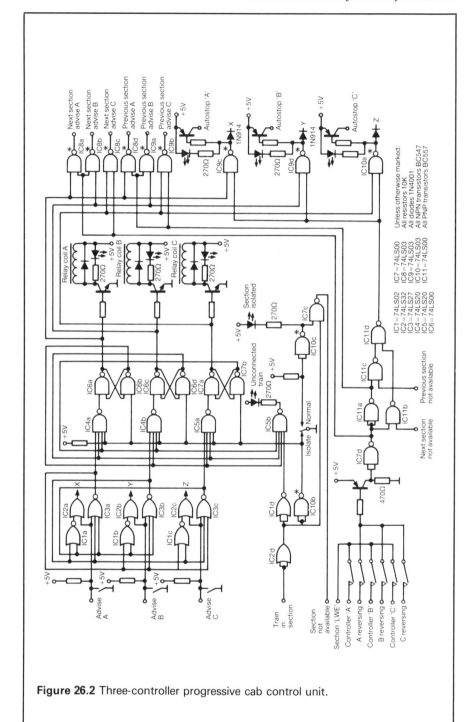

Figure 26.2 Three-controller progressive cab control unit.

the other. If both inputs are activated simultaneously, NOR gate IC1b applies a '1' to one input of the NAND gates IC2a and IC2b. The one of these whose other input is derived from the *selected* advise line will activate the 'autostop' output transistor, T4 or T5, for the *other,* ie non-selected, controller. The selected advise input, now a logical '1' is applied to a three-input NAND gate, IC3a or IC3b. These gates only give a '0' output when, besides having the advise input, the section is occupied and not isolated, and the other controller is not connected to it. A logical '0' from the output of IC3a or IC3b trips one of the two SR bistables made up from the four NAND gates in IC4. The tripped bistable provides bias for one or other of the relay-drive transistors T1 and T2. These energise the relay coil and the 'A connected' or 'B connected' LED. T1 and T2 may need to be Darlington pairs. The relay coils may be driven from a separate power supply if it is inconvenient for them to share the 5 V TTL supply.

The relays need a minimum of DPST contacts which 'make' when the coil is energised. The contacts should be capable of carrying 1 A for use with OO/HO and smaller gauges. However, very rarely are the contacts called upon to switch such high current.

From the foregoing, a relay coil becomes energised only when (i) the appropriate 'advise' input is activated, and (ii) the section is occupied and not isolated and (iii) the other relay is not energised. These conditions are met briefly when a train enters the section from an adjacent section having a similar unit.

Once tripped, the bistable can only be reset by the vacating of the section or the throwing of the 'isolate' switch to the 'isolate' position.

(ii) Occupation/isolation circuitry. This is a group of related functions served by the circuitry around IC1d, IC3c, IC5a, IC5b and IC6a.

When the section is occupied, a logical '0' from the track circuit is applied to the input of IC5a, which is used as an inverter to apply a '1' to IC3a and IC3b in the controller selector circuit. An open-collector output is essential for IC5a, as the closing of the 'isolate' switch short-circuits the output of this gate. When the 'isolate' switch is in the 'isolate' position, the input of IC5b goes 'high' and its output 'low', lighting the 'section isolated' LED and also applying a '0' to one input of IC6a. The occupation of the section applies a '0' to the other input of IC6a. So, if the section is isolated or occupied (or both), IC6a delivers a '1' output which feeds the 'section unavailable' output.

The spare NOR gate IC1d is used as an inverter to apply a '1' when the section is occupied to one input of IC3c. This gate only delivers a 'low' output, lighting the 'unconnected train LED', when the section is occupied and neither controller connected to it.

(iii) Direction-sensing circuitry. To simplify the electronics, spare relay contacts are used to select the 'reverse-engaged' output of the connected controller. Provided that the controller has positive-going output before the reversing switch (or relay contacts), its negative supply will always be negative relative to the PCC system's *positive* supply (work it out for yourself if you don't believe me). So, a connection to the controller's negative line via the relay contacts will bias T3 into conduction applying a '1' to the input of IC6b, used as an inverter. Thus, a '1' from its output means 'forward selected'. Its output is applied to the inputs of IC6c, used as a further inverter, so a '1' from the output of this means 'reverse selected'.

(iv) Output arrangements. The four NAND gates in IC7 service the four 'advise' outputs drawing their inputs from the controller-selection bistables and the direction-sensing circuitry. Open-collector gates are used as these outputs often find themselves paralleled and short-circuited by the 'advise' switches of adjacent units.

Besides the interlock facility described earlier, which operates when both 'advise' inputs are activated simultaneously, another system is provided by IC5c, IC5d, IC6d, IC2c and IC2d. If the next section towards which a train is heading is isolated or occupied, the appropriate autostop will be activated. Transistors T4 and T5 are essential in the 'autostop' output circuit as they feed into a controller circuit which may be at a potential more negative than that of the PCC negative supply.

Three-controller version

Figure 26.2 shows the circuit of a three-controller version offering the same facilities. Note that this circuit uses 11 ICs in contrast with the seven for the two-controller version.

Simplifications

The unit described is emphatically a de-luxe, full-feature unit. Many simplifications are possible if you are willing to sacrifice some of the facilities. Ultimately, only the controller selector circuitry and most of the occupation/isolation circuitry are essential. For example, if you do not want the 'autostop' facilities, you can dispense with IC1b, IC2, IC5c, IC5d, IC6a, IC6d, T4, T5 and associated components. You can also remove the direction-sensing circuitry if your trains run consistently in the same direction, eg on a multiple-track main line. The second pair of relay contacts and the circuitry around T3, IC6b and IC6c now disappear. In its simplest form you can eliminate IC7 as well. You take your 'advise' outputs from the outputs of IC4b and IC4c and apply these direct to the inputs of the next section's unit only. The system will work as long as trains run forward and you will be able to reverse normally *within a section* but trains will not be able to reverse from one section to another unless you fit open-collector buffers into the 'advise' lines and activate the 'advise' buttons manually as the train crosses the 'borders'.

With an intermediate level of sophistication you can arrange for each unit to apply its 'advise' outputs to the units both in advance and in rear to permit bidirectional running but you will need to introduce AND gates or buffers between the outputs and inputs or otherwise the 'advise' signals will be passed on down the line to other units where they are not wanted. With TTL you cannot use blocking diodes.

Main line running

I am now assuming once more that you are using the full-feature unit. Installation is simplest in main-line blocks, but even here you must be careful about inter-connecting your units. The 'advise A' input, for instance, must be connected to *both* the 'next block advise A' output of the previous block's unit *and* the 'previous block advise A' output of the *next* block's unit. The same will apply to the corresponding B outputs and input (and C, if applicable).

Termini

If our section is in a terminus, one set of 'advise' outputs will not be needed and either the 'next section unavailable' or the 'previous section unavailable' input should be wired to supply positive via a pull-up resistor to give a permanent 'section unavailable' input. Thus, a train entering the section will automatically have its controller's 'autostop' activated. If the train stops short of its destination, the controller's 'autostop cancel' switch should be used to over-ride the interlock and get the train home.

Junctions

Junctions pose many complications in the installation of PCC. The simplest way to handle them is as follows. Outputs, e.g 'next section advise A' or 'this section unavailable', may be fanned out to many other units, the limit being the fan out of TTL (see Appendix 4). Thus, if our section ends in a facing junction, giving a choice of two possible 'next sections', we apply our 'advise input' to *both* but we may do some selecting on the inputs of the units of those two next sections. Where a section has a choice of inputs, eg if there is a trailing junction at one end, so that trains may enter our section from two different lines, the unit's inputs should be selected using, for instance, the 74LS157 quad two-input data selector which we met in Chapter 18. Its select input is derived, as before, from the setting of the turnout. In this way only the relevant data will be fed into the unit.

Using the units

The unit described in detail is for two controllers only; we called them A and B. We also looked at the circuit for a three-controller version; we called the controllers A, B and C.

It may seem that the restriction of a complex layout to two or three controllers only is rather limiting but remember that it is only those *sections* of

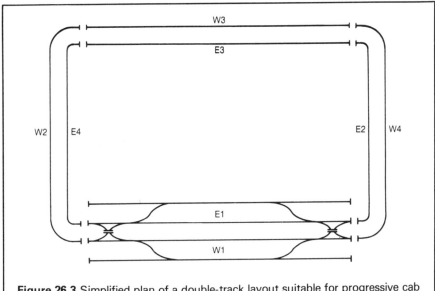

Figure 26.3 Simplified plan of a double-track layout suitable for progressive cab control.

the layout that were restricted to two or three controllers; the total layout may have many more controllers. Indeed, with a little ingenuity this PCC system permits endless combinations and permutations.

Consider the layout shown in simplified form in Figure 26.3. Basically it is a double-track oval, each track being divided into four sections. In E1 and W1, which represent the site of a main station, the tracks include passing loops, crossovers and sidings. It would be very easy to organise this layout using PCC for operation with *five* controllers, A, B, C, D and X. We should need six two-controller units and two three-controller units. Controllers A and B are dedicated to running on the westbound (clockwise) line (W1 to W4) and controllers C and D to the eastbound line (E1 to E4). Controller X is only used for movements within the main station area (E1 and W1). So, the three-controller units are for sections E1 and W1; the other six sections have the two-controller units. Thus, we could easily have four trains running simultaneously on the main lines and still have controller X in reserve while there could be other trains or pilot locos waiting isolated in the loops and sidings in the main station area.

Controller X is used when we want to pass a train from the eastbound to the westbound lines and *vice versa*. Imagine a train drawing into the station (W1) from W4 and powered by controller A. As soon as it is stopped, the PCC unit for W1 is isolated, restored and controller X selected. The loco can now run round its train and be coupled up at the other end. The crossover turnouts are set for E2 and the train is restarted for E2. The train can pass from W1 into E1 using controller X without difficulty, but cannot proceed into E2, since controller X is not on E2's 'menu'. So, as the train crosses the rail breaks at the intersection you will need to press the 'advise C' or 'advise D' button on E2's PCC unit. The train will now be able to run indefinitely on the eastbound line with the selected controller. Alternatively, you could arrange for X-controlled trains entering E2 always to 'pick up' controller C (or controller D), simply by making connections between the appropriate 'advise' outputs and inputs.

On a very large layout — too large for any one operator to oversee — there may be several operators located at strategic points. Each operator looks after a limited area of the layout, say, ten sections. Each has two (or three) controllers selected by the PCC system described. At the intersections of areas, trains pass not only from one section to another but also from one controller to another. In this way between 8 and 12 trains may be running simultaneously — but the PCC units are all two- or three-controller units.

So, as you can see, the system is very versatile indeed and probably a whole book could be written on the ways it could be used, but I'll leave that for another time!

Part 6

Train lighting systems

Many years ago some coaches in the Trix Twin range incorporated lighting; more recently lighting units have been available for the Hornby range of OO-scale coaches. The lamps are lit direct from the controller output, so, of course, brightness varies with controller setting and they cannot be left on while the train is stationary (unless you use 'Zero-One' or some other command-control system). This section of the book describes two systems for constant train lighting which is independent of the traction power. Chapter 27 details a system using high frequency AC generated in the controller itself while Chapter 28 is concerned with a scheme using rechargeable batteries. Both systems present their own individual problems, but all train lighting projects share certain difficulties.

The first concerns the nature of the light source itself. One day LED technology will greatly simplify train lighting and, indeed, I recently heard of a modeller who lit a train, apparently quite effectively, using *green* LEDs. The trouble is that white-light LEDs are not yet available (at the time of writing, late 1983) and the high-brightness yellow types which offer the most realistic alternative are expensive. You would need a great many, ideally at least one per compartment, but the wealthy amongst us might like to try it. However, until the day of cheap, bright, white-light LEDs dawns, we shall be compelled to rely mostly on tungsten lamps for train lighting. These posed few problems in the tinplate-constructed Trix coaches mentioned earlier, but tales abound among modellers of those who have filled modern coaches with tungsten lamps and sent the train off in a dazzling blaze of light only to find a few minutes later that the loco is pulling a sticky mass of molten polystyrene. Never forget that tungsten lamps run *hot;* indeed they only emit light as a product of their heat.

It is important to limit the number of lamps, so I impose an arbitrary limit of two per coach. These I position as far as possible from any plastic structures and use foil reflectors to direct the light *upwards.* As well as doing this I paint the underside of the coach roof matt white so that the light is reflected downwards fairly evenly along the length of the coach. The result is quite effective.

It also helps to under-run the lamps, ie to use a voltage lower than that specified. This does, admittedly, make the lamp less bright and more yellowish but it also keeps the lamps cooler and, for that reason, prolongs their life. Moreover, I have never suffered any melted coaches! If in doubt about the heating effects of any proposed lighting system, try out a 'mock up' on an old discarded coach body. Remember that a system which apparently stays cool in a draughty attic may not stay cool in the cramped confines of an air-tight polystyrene coach!

The second problem is concerned with electrical connections between adjacent coaches. For the high-frequency lighting system (Chapter 27) you could dispense with these altogether by giving each coach its own power pick-ups and this may well be a wise course of action. However, with the battery back-up system (Chapter 28), connections between coaches are essential since only one coach contains the batteries upon which the whole system depends. The problem is to find wires which are thick enough to conduct the fairly high currents involved but flexible enough not to cause derailments on tight curves with modern lightweight coaches. If you can obtain a supply of it, the wire used with personal earphones is ideal. You may be tempted to use Litz wire, intended for coil winding, but this is difficult to solder and may present heating problems when conducting currents in hundreds of milliAmps. If all else fails, use standard sleeved multi-strand connecting wire coiled up like the leads to telephone handsets. You can achieve this by winding it tightly around the shaft of a miniature screwdriver. These connecting wires can be fitted with a soldercon pin at each end which plug into further soldercon pins fixed beneath each end of each coach. This provides a means whereby coaches can be separated quite easily if the train formation is to be changed.

The last problem concerns the controller power supply. When you add 0.5 A of lighting load to the existing traction load you may find that your overload cut-out operates with rather less provocation than previously, eg whenever a lit train climbs a gradient. (This is less likely to happen with the high-frequency system in which some of the lighting load is borne by a separate power supply.) The only solution is to fit a higher-rated circuit breaker and, if your transformer starts to glow faintly, to use a higher rated power supply.

Chapter 27: Improved high-frequency train lighting system

Most high-frequency (HF) train lighting systems use a separate HF AC generator whose output is connected in parallel with that of the controller to put HF power on to the track. By using HF power (30 kHz is the frequency most often used) it is possible to isolate the traction power and the lighting power at the train very simply. The motor, being an inductive device, presents a high impedance to the HF power and is therefore hardly affected by it; a suitable capacitor in series with each lamp prevents the controller output from affecting the lighting, while the HF power passes readily through the capacitors to the lamps where it is needed.

Two difficulties attend this arrangement. Firstly, there is the danger that the controller itself, especially at high speed settings, will short-circuit the HF generator's output. This is usually remedied by inserting a choke coil in series with the controller output, but this can cause appreciable traction voltage loss when the load is heavy. Secondly, to light a long train or several trains considerable HF power is needed and the HF generator is likely to become as complex and expensive as the controller itself. There is, as often, a single solution to both problems. We generate the HF pulses in the heart of the controller itself, so that the same output stage handles both sets of pulses simultaneously. All of its power handling capacity (subject to the controller's

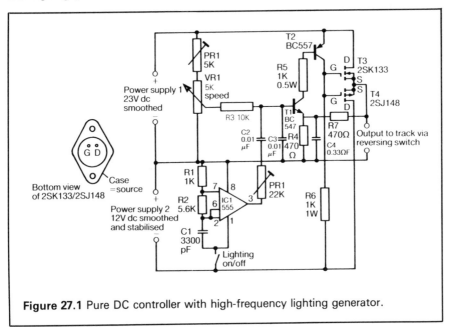

Figure 27.1 Pure DC controller with high-frequency lighting generator.

overload cut-out threshold) is available to handle lighting or traction current according to load.

Practical problems

This Chapter describes an attempt to modify a closed-loop controller, resembling that of Chapter 1, by adding a HF generator consisting of a 555 timer IC set up as a free-running multivibrator at 30 kHz. The complete circuit is shown in Figure 27.1. The feedback loop (R7/R4) is decoupled to AC by C4 so that the *mean* output voltage is determined by the control voltage set by the speed control VR1, while the instantaneous output voltage is free to make the temporary excursions associated with delivering the HF AC output.

Unfortunately, although the scheme sounds simple enough, it is fraught with complications. For example, if we are to deliver AC while the DC output is nil, ie if we want to stop a train but keep its lights on, the output must be capable of delivering negative-going as well as positive-going excursions of power, so that the mean output remains nil. This demands that we use a split power supply or, as in my prototype, two power supplies in series. Furthermore, to deliver true AC which is capable of alternately charging and discharging a capacitive load demands push-pull output but this causes the reappearance in a different guise of the short-circuiting problem associated with the traditional type of high-frequency lighting system. All attempts at making heavy-duty bipolar power transistors deliver a steady 30 kHz failed. Even though theoretically impossible, both transistors of the pair would become conductive simultaneously leading to very heavy current drain from both power supplies and considerable heating of the transistors. The process then became regenerative, the heating making the transistors more conductive and *vice versa,* a well known effect called *thermal runaway.* To protect the transistors it was essential that the circuit be operated for no longer than two minutes at a time. Clearly such a circuit was of no practical use.

The problem was solved by replacing the bipolar output transistors with VMOS power FETs. These are expensive (I paid £7.50 for the complementary pair) but are ideally suited to HF work and quite free from thermal runaway.

VMOS FETs

The 2SJ148 (sometimes marked J48) is a p-channel enhancement-mode device. It behaves like a pnp power transistor except that it presents infinite input resistance on its gate and, when conductive, will conduct drain current in either direction. The 2SK133 (sometimes marked K33) is an n-channel enhancement-mode device, which behaves like an npn power transistor with the same exceptions as before. Both are rated for drain currents up to 7 A.

Care should be taken in handling these devices. They are not nearly so susceptible to damage by static charges as are small-signal MOSFETs and CMOS ICs but even so it is best to avoid handling them in hot, dry environments. Fingers or soldering irons should always be touched to an earth point before contact with the gate or drain terminals. The sources of these devices are connected to the metal can, which is convenient, since both devices may be bolted direct to the same heat sink. *In this circuit it is essential that both devices be mounted on a heat sink.*

The two devices are used as source followers only and so give no voltage gain. T2 replaces the output Darlington of Chapter 1 and T3/T4 act as buffers to ensure that ample current is available at any output voltage. Resistor R6 provides pull-down to the level of the negative terminal of the power supply, to facilitate negative-going excursions of output.

Performance of the circuit

It must be stated that this circuit did not work as well as was intended. The prototype suffered a leakage current of 25 mA, which, at least, was steady and negligible compared to that experienced with bipolar output transistors. In general, while the circuit did permit the independent operation of train lights and running of locomotives, there was some interference. The lights were brightest with the train stopped and they dimmed perceptibly as the train ran and gained speed. At full speed they were extinguished altogether, but with this controller full speed is unprototypically high and R3 should be chosen for a reasonable compromise of maximum speed and acceptable minimum brightness. Switching the lights on while the train is running causes a noticeable slowing of the train.

Nearly all tests were carried out using 12 V lamps for lighting and the brightness was adequate but not dazzling. A few tests were carried out using 6 V miniature bulbs, which were far brighter and less susceptible to variation of brightness. It is recommended that train lighting for use with this system use 6 V bulbs. If they show evidence of being over-run, ie of having a short operating life, the value of the series capacitors should be reduced, eg to 0.047 μF. In general the circuit poses few other problems than those already described. C3 appears redundant and yet *is* essential. Without it the controller is prone to burst into supersonic oscillation so that lights come on even with the light switch off. PR1 provides some adjustment of brightness to prevent

HF overloading of the output which can cause trains to creep forward at 'stop' when the lights are on.

My prototype used two power supplies. The 'upper' supply, concerned mainly with traction, used a standard model railway controller/full-wave rectifier unit delivering 16 V at up to 2 A. This was smoothed using a 2200 μF electrolytic capacitor to give a steady 23 V, hence the high speeds obtainable. The 'lower' power supply was an adjustable stabilised supply set to 12 V and capable of delivering up to about 750 mA. This is concerned mainly with the lighting power at lower settings of the speed control, when excursions of output fall below 0 V. On no account should trains be run with the 'lower' supply off.

Using the unit

When the HF system is on, *all* train lights (including *all* those with direction-sensing diodes) will be illuminated. As mentioned above, the lamps may be 6 V to 12 V types used singly or lower-voltage types, eg 3 V, could be connected as pairs in series. All lamps or pairs of lamps should have series capacitors which may be 0.1 μF or 0.47 μF. Lower values may be used if the lamps appear excessively bright. Alternatively, LEDs may be used. These should be connected as reverse-parallel pairs with a 0.01 μF series capacitor. No series resistor is needed, since current is limited by the reactance of the capacitor (530 Ω at 30 kHz).

The HF system does not normally interfere with return-rail track circuits but behaves as a second controller so that a locomotive-less train of illuminated stock is detected as long as the HF system is on. It does, however, interfere with live-rail track circuits producing spurious 'section occupied' indications and also with speedometer circuits, causing wildly erratic readings. However, the controller itself cannot be used with either live-rail track circuits or speedometers, as it is a pure DC controller (but see Chapter 30).

Radio interference is a concomitant of HF lighting systems. Indeed, the easiest way to check the frequency at which the system is operating is to place an AM radio receiver beside your layout while the HF system is on. Tune along the long- and medium-wave broadcast bands noting the frequencies (the tuning scale should be calibrated in kHz or MHz) at which interference from the unit is heard. This will sound like a hum, hiss or squeal from the receiver and you can easily check whether any particular noise originates from your HF system by momentarily switching it off and seeing if the interference disappears. When you have logged a number of interference frequencies, you should find that they are spaced at regular intervals and that interval should be the 30 kHz or so fundamental frequency of your HF generator. Because of this radio interference please be considerate in your use of the circuit. It is unlikely to hinder reception of local radio and TV broadcasts but it may cause difficulties in the reception of distant stations in the long- and medium-wave broadcasts bands, especially if the receiver is close to your layout.

Chapter 28: Alternative constant train lighting system

The high-frequency lighting system described in Chapter 27 suffers two major disadvantages: (i) the expense of the special controller with its complementary

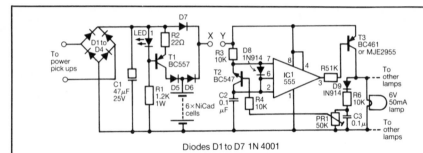

Diodes D1 to D7 1N 4001

Figure 28.1 Circuit for a battery-back-up train lighting system. Alternative switching systems, which go between X and Y, are shown in Figures 28.2 and 28.3.

Figure 28.2 Simplest option—a plain on/off switch on the coach.

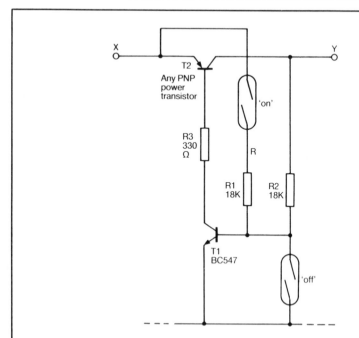

Figure 28.3 Complementary bistable used to switch the train lighting by means of magnets and reed switches.

VMOS output stage and (ii) incompatibility with live-rail track circuits, speedometers and through-the-rails sound systems (Chapter 30). This prompted me to re-examine a train lighting system described by M.H. Babani in *Electronic Circuits for Railway Modellers* (published by Bernards, London, 1977, but now out of print).

Babani lit his lamps from the controller output when it was available, but provided an auxiliary lighting supply in the form of rechargeable nickel-cadmium (NiCad) cells for those occasions when the controller output was not available, eg when the train was stationary. The controller output, when available, was also used to recharge the NiCads. I have not tried Babani's circuit, because it uses NiCads and lamps of types not easily obtainable, but it looks sound enough. Instead I devised a system operating on similar principles but using six easily obtainable 'size AA' (14.3 mm diameter × 50 mm long) NiCad cells (developing 7 V to 9 V) to drive 6 V bulbs via a 6 V switching regulator. This keeps the lighting level absolutely steady under all circumstances. The circuit was designed to run up to 10 lamps (6 V 50 mA nominal) giving a total consumption of 0.5 A.

The circuit

Figure 28.1 shows the basic circuit and Figures 28.2 and 28.3 two alternative types of on/off switching. Current from the power pick ups enters the bridge rectifier D1 to D4 making the circuit fully bidirectional while capacitor C1 smoothes the input. LED 1 is used as a voltage regulator to hold the base of T1 at about − 1.6 V over a wide range of input voltage. It only lights up when the NiCads are charging so cannot double as a tail lamp. Resistor R2 in the emitter circuit of T1 limits collector current to 50 mA, the maximum recommended charge current for the NiCads. Blocking diode D5 prevents the NiCads from discharging via T1's base/collector junction and R1. The circuit therefore provides for the NiCads to be charged and kept topped up by controller output of either polarity, provided of course that the voltage is sufficiently high. The juxtaposition of D6/D7 ensures that the lighting circuit uses as its supply whichever of the bridge rectifier output and the NiCads offers the higher voltage and consequently the circuit switches automatically between power supplies as the voltage on the track varies.

Voltage regulator

When the controller output is at a higher voltage than the NiCads (plus the drop across the bridge rectifier) the lamps run from the controller. Now, the voltage that the 6 V lamps 'see' may vary from 6 V to 16 V depending on the controller type and setting so, unless some form of voltage regulator is introduced between the lamps and their supply, the brightness of the lamps will vary with controller setting and, at higher settings, there will be a very real danger of burnout. It may seem that all that is needed is a 7806 or 7805 voltage regulator IC. Either can handle up to 0.5 A, but at higher loads even an input of 8 V causes the IC to get very hot and with an input of 15 V at a load of 0.5 A a 7805 would be called upon to dissipate an intolerable 5 W. In fact, the ICs contain in-built protection against such overloads and they simply shut down, but not before they get hot enough to melt polystyrene coaches! I did experiment using a 7805 with an array of 12 V lamps in parallel; these light up as the voltage across the regulator rises and thereby dissipate some of the waste power as light. Although this arrangement showed promise it also caused some loss of regulation with resultant fluctuations of brightness in the lighting lamps. Moreover, as a circuit, it was clumsy.

More elegant is the circuit I finally adopted which employs a switching regulator circuit (around IC1, T2 and T3 in Figure 28.1). This is a voltage regulator which works by pulse width modulation and in which the output transistor does not get hot. IC1 is a 555 timer IC1 set up as a free-running multivibrator. The charge-up period of timing capacitor C2 is fixed at about 0.1ms (R3 × C2, D8 being negligible) but the discharge period is variable, depending on the bias applied to T2. T2 really should be npn and apparently 'upside down' in this application. Remember that it is bypassed by D8 during charge-up periods while its emitter is shorted to ground via pin 7 during discharge periods. It is during discharges that T3 is enabled. Feedback loop D9/R6/C3 (chosen to have the same time constant as R3/D8/C2) provides efficient regulations of the output voltage, which is adjustable by means of VR1.

On/off switching

A facility is needed for switching the lighting off, otherwise the lighting will rapidly discharge the NiCads when the train is not in use. This must be connected between X and Y in Figure 28.1. The simplest alternative, shown in Figure 28.2, is to use a plain on/off switch somewhere on the coach in which the circuitry is installed. Probably the best places for the switch are underneath or tucked inside a gangway connection. The alternative is to replace the switch by the complementary bistable shown in Figure 28.3. This is activated by a pair of normally open reed switches, one for the 'on' function and one for the 'off'. It is suggested that the 'on' switch be mounted just beneath the roof centre line and the 'off' switch vertically on one side of the coach. The lighting can now be turned on by placing a permanent magnet on a bridge or signal gantry beneath which the train is to pass. Better still an electromagnet in the same position may be energised from the control panel if it is desired to run the lighting. To turn the lighting off, the train must pass a permanent magnet or an energised electromagnet in some structure alongside the track. Do ensure that the correct side of the vehicle is presented to the magnet or, alternatively, use parallel reed switches, one on each side of the vehicle.

Practical considerations

The main problem is finding accomodation in the train for the NiCads. Babani used smaller cells and managed to conceal them in the kitchen section of a restaurant car (OO scale). Mine were contained in a battery box from Maplin Electronic Supplies Ltd (catologue number YR62S) which measures 158 × 28 × 16 mm (empty). The only OO-scale passenger vehicle in which this could be easily concealed is the Lima BR Mk I full brake and then only after the removal of the partitions around the guard's compartment. Fortunately this vehicle has few windows so that its unprototypical load is not obvious.

Even so, stowage of the battery box poses mechanical problems. The box is wider than 28 mm when the cells have been inserted since they protrude out of the edges. Thus, the box will not lie flat on the car floor but if you lean it on its side its weight overbalances the vehicle so that the underneath of the floor rubs on the bogie wheels, preventing easy movement. The only answer is to use blocks of wood or plastic to balance the box on its edge up the centre of the car. Lima vehicles are particularly well suited to lighting since it is easy to fit power pick ups to their solid metal wheels.

The electronics can easily be installed on pieces of Veroboard at either end of the car but try to keep the voltage regulator output transistor away from any plastic structures. If you wish to recharge the NiCads — and this may well be necessary after continuous slow running — switch the lighting off before placing the battery coach on permanently live track.

NiCad cells

The cells used are rated at 0.5 Ah. This means that in theory on a full charge each cell will deliver 0.5 A (500 mA) for one hour. The discharge rate should not exceed 0.5 A, hence the limit of ten 50 mA lamps. The charge rate should not exceed one tenth of the maximum discharge rate, ie 50 mA for these cells. To charge the cells from a state of total discharge might be expected to take ten times the hourly maximum discharge rate, ie 10 hours. In fact, owing to losses, it takes 14 hours at 50 mA. Lower charge rates may be used with a corresponding increase in charge time.

Part 7

Sound effects

Much has been written in the general railway modelling press about the addition of sound effects to model railways and there are many ways of doing this, some demanding no knowledge of electronics at all. For instance, if you are an adept with tape recorders, you can easily make up a loop of tape containing train sounds (either your own recordings or dubbed off some of the excellent commercial recordings available) and play the loop, gradually advancing the volume control as the train approaches and fading it as the train goes away. Paul Towers, whose exhibition layout depicts a narrow-gauge line in a very rural environment, insists on playing a background tape of bird song, which is understandable as Paul is also a keen ornithologist. Recorded station announcements can be replayed through a miniature speaker concealed in a station building or the roar of traffic and shouts of market traders could be reproduced in the town square; the possibilities are endless.

In this book, however, we are committed to the use of electronic techniques. The rapid development of computerised games with built-in sound effects has brought a benefit to our hobby in the availability of ICs that generate a wide range of complex sounds with a minimum of external components. Chapter 29 describes in detail the use of one of the smallest and cheapest of these ICs, the Texas Instruments SN94281. Chapter 30 discusses three ways in which the sounds generated can be reproduced on a model railway.

Chapter 29: Sound generation

Of several complex sound generator ICs on the market I have concentrated on the use of just one in the sound systems to be described, the Texas Instruments SN94281. This is because: (i) this IC is very small, being contained in the standard 16-pin dual-in-line package, which enables it to fit with ease in OO/HO vehicles if required; (ii) as a consequence of its 16-pin configuration it is easy to use, requiring a minimum of external components and yet offering a very wide range of sounds; and (iii) it is fairly cheap and readily available, eg from Tandy ('Radio Shack') stores.

The 94281 comprises a super low-frequency oscillator (SLFO) whose frequency of oscillation is dependent solely on the values of two external components, a voltage-controlled oscillator (VCO) whose fundamental frequency of operation is set by two external components or by those components and a voltage which may be externally derived or derived from the SLFO, a pseudo-random white noise generator (NG) with low-pass filter, a mixer system which allows the selection of any one or any combination of the three sound sources, an electronic volume control and an amplifier capable of delivering 125 mW of audio into an 8 Ω load. The IC requires a 9 V smoothed power supply. A 5 V stabiliser is included in the IC and its output is available for a limited quantity of external peripheral circuitry, eg logic systems, timers. It may seem as though two oscillators and a white noise generator are somewhat limited in their capabilities, yet, because they can be made to react with each other, the range of quite convincing model railway sounds that can be produced is remarkable. We shall look at each section of the IC in turn.

The super low-frequency oscillator (SLFO)
This will oscillate over the range 0.1 Hz to 20 kHz, the frequency being set by the SLFO resistor, R_s (between pin 11 and ground), and the SLFO capacitor C_s (between pin 12 and ground) according to the following equation:

$$\text{Frequency (Hz)} = \frac{0.66}{(R_s + 9k) \times C_s}$$

where R_s is in Ohms and C_s is in Farads. The output fed to the mixer is a 50 per cent duty cycle square wave. A triangular wave is fed to the VCO input via a select control activated by pin 13. If pin 13 is low (for an explanation see later) this triangular wave will modulate the VCO frequency; if pin 13 is high the SLFO will have no effect on the VCO.

The voltage controlled oscillator (VCO)
This covers a range from below 1 Hz to over 20 kHz. There are three ways in which its frequency of oscillation can be set.

(i) With pin 13 high the VCO will deliver a steady tone set by the VCO capacitor, C_v (between pin 9 and ground), and the VCO resistor, R_v (between pin 10 and ground). The frequency is then determined by the equation:

$$\text{Frequency (Hz)} = \frac{1.61}{(R_v + 9k) \times C_v}$$

where R_v is in Ohms and C_v in Farads.

(ii) With pin 13 low and the SLFO in operation, the triangular waveform caused by the alternate charge and discharge of C_s can be used to modulate the frequency of the VCO. As the applied voltage increases, the VCO frequency falls. As the applied voltage decreases, the frequency of the VCO rises. The sweep range is about 10:1, the *minimum* frequency being determined by the equation:

$$\text{Frequency (Hz)} = \frac{0.6}{(R_v + 9k) \times C_v}$$

where R_v is in Ohms and C_v in Farads.

(iii) With pin 13 low and the SLFO *not* operating (it is disabled by the removal of R_s or C_s), the VCO frequency can be voltage controlled by applying an external voltage (V_{ext}) to pin 12 (normally C_s). The value of V_{ext} must be in the range 0 to 2.3 V. The frequency of operation is now determined as follows:

Frequency (Hz) = $\dfrac{1.45}{(R_v + 9k) \times C_v \times (V_{ext} - 0.1)}$

where R_v is in Ohms, C_v is in Farads and V_{ext} is in Volts.

Like the SLFO, the VCO generates a square-wave output having a 50 per cent duty cycle.

Noise generator (NG)

This produces random square waves, ie a wide mix of frequencies. Unfiltered it sounds like a hiss, but high frequencies can be filtered out using the noise filter. Cut-off point of the filter is determined by the noise filter resistor, R_n (between pin 2 and ground) and the noise filter capacitor, C_n (between pin 1 and ground) according to the following equation:

$$F_{cut\text{-}off}\,(Hz) = \frac{0.43}{(R_n + 9k) \times C_n}$$

where R_n is in Ohms and C_n is in Farads.

Selector

The selector is controlled by three pins (Nos 14, 15 and 16) and determines which sound sources are admitted to the output amplifier. There are two factors which must be taken into account when considering this circuit.

(i) Although the selector operates from a 5 V supply and its inputs are referred to as '0's and '1's recalling TTL practice (see Appendix 4), the inputs do not behave like normal TTL inputs. An unconnected input on the 94281 is regarded as a '0'. Only if the input is connected to the 5 V rail (available at pin 4) is it regarded as a '1'. The inputs can, however, be controlled from normal (push-pull) TTL outputs if required.

(ii) When two or more sounds are combined in the 94281's mixer, the resulting complex sound is not the *sum* but the *product* of the inputs. All three sound sources generate square waves at 5 V; the selector treats them as digital signals being applied to an AND gate. Only while all the selected sound sources are high is the output high. So, if we select, say, the SLFO at 4 Hz and the NG, the combined output will consist of bursts of noise, each burst coming while the SLFO output is high; it will sound like a steam loco chuffing. The following table shows how the selector controls relate to the eight possible combinations of sound sources.

pin 14	pin 15	pin 16	
0	0	0	VCO only
0	0	1	SLFO only
0	1	0	NG only
0	1	1	VCO and NG
1	0	0	SLFO and NG
1	0	1	SLFO and VCO and NG
1	1	0	SLFO and VCO
1	1	1	inhibit

It is possible that we might want two sounds simultaneously. For instance, I described above how the SLFO and NG can be used to simulate a steam loco 'chuff' sound but we could also set up the VCO at about 1 kHz as a whistle. For the chuffer the selector inputs are 100; for the whistle the inputs are 000. How can we have both sounds simultaneously, ie a steam loco chuffing and whistling? *Not* by using code 101 (SLFO, VCO and NG); since the AND function affects the whistle as well as the escaping steam, so the whistle will be silenced between chuffs. The answer is by high-frequency multiplexing, ie rapidly alternating between the two sets of inputs. In this instance it is only necessary to pulse the input applied to pin 14 since this will give the required alternation between inputs 000 and 100. By varying the duty cycle of the multiplexed input, the relative loudness of the two sounds can be adjusted. The input pulses could be derived from a 555 timer IC set up as a free-running multivibrator.

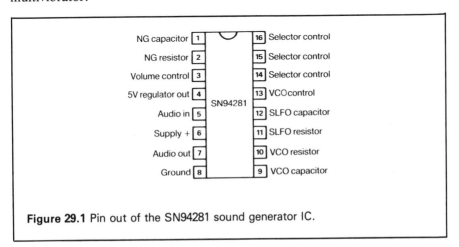

Figure 29.1 Pin out of the SN94281 sound generator IC.

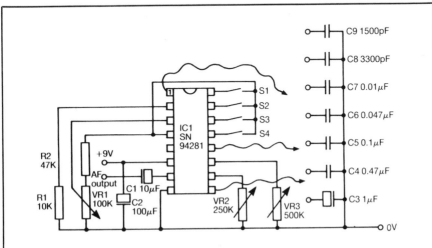

Figure 29.2 Test bed for the 94281. The flying leads from pins 1, 9 and 12 can be connected to any of the array of capacitors in the 'capacitor bar'.

Volume control

An electronic volume control is provided by means of pin 3. The voltage applied to this pin should be adjustable from 3.5 V for full volume down to 0.4 V for no sound. Pin 3 must not be taken above 5 V nor below 0 V or damage to the IC may result.

Although none of the circuits described in this chapter uses the facility, the volume control could be used in conjunction with other circuitry to provide sounds requiring certain decay characteristics, eg bells and explosions.

Amplifier

The IC contains an on-board audio amplifier having push-pull output capable of delivering 125 mA into a capacitively coupled 8 Ω load. Output is provided on pin 7. The amplifier is also provided with an input (pin 5) to which external signals may be applied to be summed with the ICs own sounds. Inputs must be current inputs, not voltage inputs. Voltage inputs should be converted to current inputs by means of a series resistor to give an input current not exceeding ± 100 μA.

Pin out of the SN94281 is given in Figure 29.1.

Analysing the SN94281

I recommend that, having purchased one or more 94281s, you build a 'test bed' for them as follows. All you need is a fairly small piece of Veroboard, a 16-pin DIL (dual-in-line) IC socket, or its equivalent in Soldercon pins, an array of capacitors (I used 1 μF, 0.47 μF, 0.1 μF, 0.047 μF, 0.01 μF, 3000 pF and 1500 pF), three potentiometers (I used 500 K for R_s, 250 K for R_v and 100 K for the volume control), a 10 K resistor for R_n and a coupling capacitor for the output: 100 μF if driving a speaker direct, otherwise 10 μF.

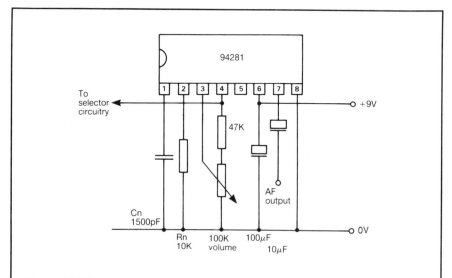

Figure 29.3 How pins 1 to 8 of the 94281 should be connected for the railway sound effects described in this Chapter. See Figures 29.4 to 29.7 for the wiring of pins 9 to 16.

I connected flying leads with crocodile clips to pins 1 (C_n), 9 (C_v) and 12 (C_x) which meant that I could select any of my array of capacitors for any of these functions, providing of course that it was not already in use. I used miniature plugs (soldercon pins) on flying leads and an array of miniature sockets (also soldercon pins) for my selector control functions (pins 13 to 16).

With this IC you *must* have a decoupling capacitor across the supply (pin 6 to ground). I used 100 μF. Without this the IC becomes terribly unstable and *damage may be caused to it*. With this in place the 94281 is stable, predictable and generally very easy to use. This arrangement enables you to 'play' with the IC and discover its capabilities in a practical manner. I began by feeding its output into a hi-fi system to get a good idea of just what the sounds were like. Later I used the IC's output direct in a miniature speaker. Keep the test bed made up. When you finalise on a circuit design, remove the IC and make up a dedicated circuit board for it. Then put another 94281 into the test bed for checking out before building its own circuit.

One tip — keep R_s and R_v high. This (i) enables you to keep C_s and C_v low, saving space, and (ii) counteracts variations in the internal resistances in the ICs. The internal 9 K series resistors do vary somewhat from chip to chip.

Some model railway sounds

Except where otherwise stated for all of the sounds described in this Chapter pins 1 to 8 of the IC are used identically as shown in Figure 29.3. For simplicity only pins 9 to 16 will be shown in Figures 29.4 to 29.7.

(i) *Steam locomotive chuff and whistle.* The SLFO controls the chuff rate and the VCO is used as the whistle. For manual operations R_s can be a 500 K pot, although it will not be possible to reduce the chuff rate below about 1 Hz. To reduce the chuff rate to zero, ie stop the SLFO, R_s must be made infinite; a simple way to do this will be considered in the next Chapter. No facility is provided in this circuit for varying the duty cycle, ie simulating different cut-offs but in practice the fixed 50 per cent duty cycle generally sounds acceptable. The chuff 'pitch' can be deepened by increasing C_n.

To sound the whistle, switch S1 must be opened. R_v, the 250 K pot, sets the whistle pitch. Opening the switch silences the chuffs, but this is not obtrusive, since the SLFO continues to run and so when S1 is closed the chuffs are resumed at exactly the right point in the cycle.

(ii) *Diesel locomotive.* Diesel locomotives are quite variable in the sounds they make, but a broadly acceptable diesel sound is provided by the very simple circuit shown in Figure 29.5. Even C_n and R_n may be omitted since the NG is not used. The sound consists of the output of the VCO set for a minimum frequency of about 40 Hz (R_v set to maximum resistance), but being swept up to about 400 Hz by the SLFO running at a frequency set by R_s. With R_s at maximum this gives an idle speed of about 5 Hz. The resultant sound has the characteristic throaty 'throb', the rate of which can be increased by adjusting R_s to simulate acceleration.

(iii) *Brake squeal/wheel screech.* Oddly enough, the circuit for this sound is identical to that for the diesel locomotive (Figure 29.5) but both R_s and R_v are set to much lower resistance, so that both oscillators operate in the range 500 to 5000 Hz. However, since the SLFO is still attempting to sweep the VCO, the result is an ear-splitting jarring screech which can be adjusted by manipulation

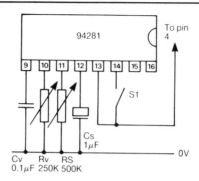

Figure 29.4 The 94281 set up as a steam loco 'chuffer' with whistle. S1 is closed for chuffs, open for whistle. For the disposition of pins 1 to 8 see Figure 29.3.

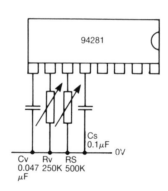

Figure 29.5 The 94281 set up as either a diesel locomotive (both Rs high) or as squeaky brakes (both Rs low). For the disposition of pins 1 to 8 see Figure 29.3.

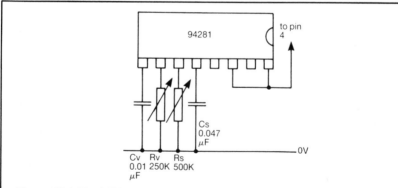

Figure 29.6 The 94281 set up as a diesel multiple unit. For the disposition of pins 1 to 8 see Figure 29.3.

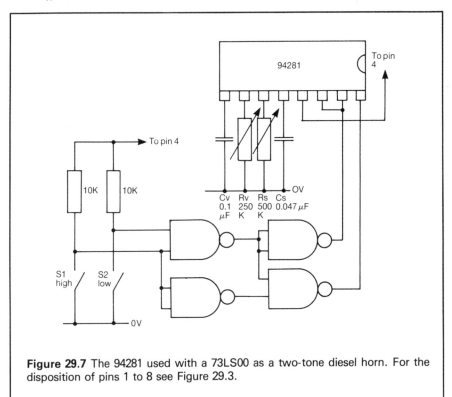

Figure 29.7 The 94281 used with a 73LS00 as a two-tone diesel horn. For the disposition of pins 1 to 8 see Figure 29.3.

of the two variable resistors. This sound is quite a good approximation of brake squeal or of the ring of tortured railway wheels on tight curves.

(iv) *Diesel multiple unit.* I confess to a fondness for DMUs and, since I ride on them regularly, am familiar with their characteristic noises. This time we select the product of all three sound sources and let the SLFO sweep the VCO (Figure 29.6). The SLFO idles at about 5 Hz sweeping the VCO between 200 and 2000 Hz although much of the VCO's output is lost in the 'mush' from the NG. The resultant sound is best described as a rhythmic, uneven rattle, instantly recognisable to devotees of six-cylinder diesel engines. The 'engine' can be revved a little by adjusting R_s but after only a little 'throttle' do the two oscillators hit the same frequency producing a throaty 'rasp', not unlike the 'snarl' beloved by all who live in the vicinity of lines where DMUs accelerate!

(v) *Two-tone diesel horn.* Not an easy sound to simulate, this, since the 94281 is best suited to continuous sounds; this demands some complex switching provided by an ancillary 74LS00 (Figure 29.7). The higher tone is provided by the VCO and the lower by the SLFO. Closing the 'high' switch accesses the VCO, irrespective of the status of the 'low' switch. Closing the 'low' switch, provided that the 'high' switch is open, accesses the SLFO. If both switches are open, the IC is disabled.

In the next Chapter we shall consider the question of what to do with the sounds having generated them.

Chapter 30: Reproduction of sound effects

In Chapter 29 we saw how quite realistic sounds — or their electrical analogue — could be generated using a small and comparatively inexpensive IC but we got no further than deriving our audio signal. What do we do with it? There are two possibilities: (i) reproducing the sound via one or more fixed loudspeakers in the vicinity of the layout and (ii) reproducing the sound via a miniature speaker on board the model train itself. We shall refer to these alternatives as off-train reproduction and on-train reproduction respectively.

Off-train reproduction

Your sound generator circuit will probably be closely associated with your controller circuitry, so that 'chuff' rate or 'diesel throb' rate is proportional to train speed. In fact, you *could* take the output of the SN94281 straight from pin 7 through a suitable capacitor (100 μF or greater) into an 8 Ω speaker, but the volume available is limited (125 mW). It might suffice if your layout is in a small room, but in an exhibition setting the sound would certainly be lost amidst the general hubbub.

For most practical purposes you will need an external audio amplifier capable of delivering at least 3 W. I have seen portable stereo radio/cassette recorders in use, although you may have to set the machine to record and then press the pause button in order to use it as a straight-through amplifier. Most likely a small hi-fi amplifier will be used and it is a good idea to position the speaker(s) beneath the layout facing downwards so that the sound is reflected upwards from the floor. This avoids the impression that the sound is coming from one or two fixed locations on the layout.

In practice, human perception of sights and sounds are linked inside the brain. Thus, if you see a model train running on a layout and you hear a train sound at the same time, the brain associates the two so that the sound seems to be coming from the train — even though in reality it is coming from a speaker some distance away.

Dealing with the sounds made by more than one train is more complex. You will need one IC for each train, each synchronised to the appropriate controller but beware of overloading the amplifier input, which will result in distortion. Use the IC's own volume control to reduce the IC's output if necessary. Figure 30.1 shows how outputs from one or more ICs can be connected to a stereo amplifier.

On-train reproduction

Sounds may be reproduced on board the train by installing in it a miniature loudspeaker. Ideally this should be situated in the locomotive itself, but it could alternatively be located in the tender or in an adjacent coach or wagon.

There are several methods of getting the audio output from the 94281 to the on-train speaker. Since the IC is small and can drive a loudspeaker direct it is perfectly feasible to install an entire sound effects system in a train (HO/OO scales upwards). This is the first system that we shall consider. Alternatively, the 94281 may be located off the train — probably in or near the controller — and its output transmitted to the train for on-train reproduction. The simplest method is to use a pure DC controller and apply the audio signal to its input in parallel with the DC control voltage. Consequently the audio signal is amplified and reproduced at the controller output superimposed on the DC for

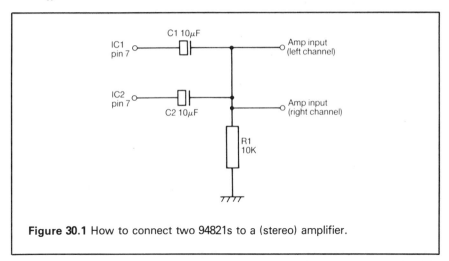

Figure 30.1 How to connect two 94821s to a (stereo) amplifier.

the motor. The system is analogous to the HF lighting scheme described in Chapter 27; indeed, my prototype used the same controller with minimal modification. This is the second system that we shall consider.

Two other systems that I have pondered using, but not tried, are as follows: (i) Use a power amplifier to drive an induction loop around the layout. The magnetic flux could be picked up by a hearing-aid-type T-coil on board the train and reproduced using an on-train amplifier, but an obvious difficulty would be interference from the magnetic field around the train motor. Furthermore, only one 'channel' would be available for the whole layout, so you could not have several trains each making a different sound, and (ii) use a radio-type technique. Install a miniature radio receiver in each train, its antenna socket being linked via a capacitor to the rails. Each 94281 output is used to modulate a carrier signal generated by a radio-frequency (RF) oscillator; the modulated RF signal is fed to the track, possibly via the controller. A very large (theoretically infinite) number of channels would be available, but again there are difficulties as there is the danger of causing highly illegal interference with radio reception, even though the RF power used need only be a few milliWatts. There is the even greater danger of interference from radio broadcasts, so that as your train passes, instead of chuffing and whistling, it delivers the ten o'clock news or Beethoven's Fifth!

Either of these systems presents the problem of constant-voltage on-train power supplies for the amplifier or radio receiver. Probably NiCad cells (see Chapter 28) would be the most satisfactory method.

On-train sound generation

This system involves installing the entire sound-effects unit in the train although not all of it needs to be in the same vehicle. It would be quite feasible, for instance, to have the speaker in the locomotive, the 94281 and associated components in the tender and the power supply in the first coach. There would, of course, need to be a number of electrical connections between the vehicles involved.

Remember that the loudspeaker will give a louder and richer output if it is mounted on some structure that acts as a baffle, ie that prevents sound waves

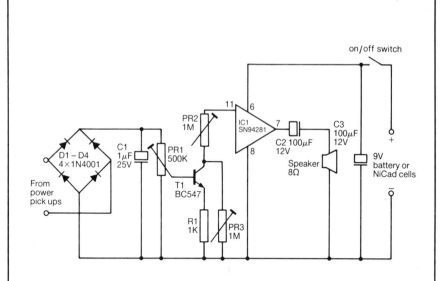

Figure 30.2 An on-train sound generator. For simplicity only four pins of the IC are shown; for the other connections see Chapter 29. PR1 sets the controller output voltage at which chuffs or acceleration begin; PR2 sets maximum chuff or sound rate: PR3 sets idling rate and is omitted if steam chuff is simulated.

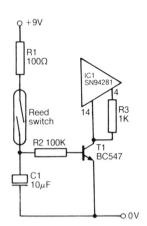

Figure 30.3 Connections that can be added to the circuit of Figure 30.1 to give a whistle when the reed switch passes over a track-mounted magnet.

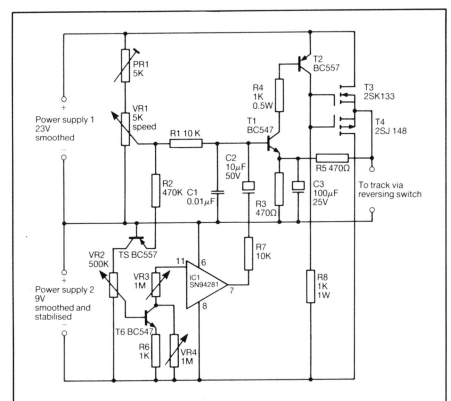

Figure 30.4 Circuit for a controller for 'through-the-rails' sound effects. Compare this circuit with that in Figure 27.1. For simplicity only four of the ICs 16 terminals are shown; for the connections to the others see Chapter 29. The circuitry around T5 and T6 provides for the 'chuff rate' (or diesel pulse rate) to be synchronised with train speed (approximately). VR2 sets the control voltage at which chuffs begin (or pulse starts to accelerate). VR3 sets maximum chuff or pulse rate. VR4 (omitted for steam chuff) sets idling rate.

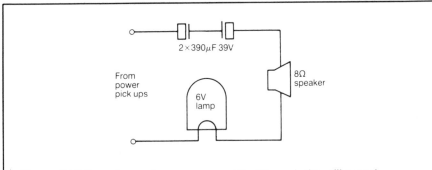

Figure 30.5 On-train speaker arrangement for 'through-the-rail' sound.

from the front of the speaker from 'short-circuiting' straight to the back of the cone. Also it is very desirable to have the cone exposed to the outside world, if at all possible. On a steam-outline locomotive it is sometimes possible to mount the speaker in the tender facing upwards through a loose sprinkling of coal over a gauze.

Do not attempt to run the 94281 from the controller output; the chances are that you will wreck the IC. Instead run it from a 9 V battery (PP3, PP4 or similar) or, better still, rechargeable nickel-cadmium cells; see Chapter 28. You will, of course, need a switch to conserve battery power when the sound is not wanted, unless you are happy to open the vehicle up and disconnect the battery at the end of each operating session. Most of the train sounds discussed in Chapter 29 demand that the SLFO be used in rough proportion to the train speed. Figure 30.2 shows a simplified on-train sound effects generator with an input from the track, so that the SLFO frequency rises as the controller output voltage rises. Pre-set resistor PR1 sets the controller output voltage threshold required to start the SLFO oscillating or to start it accelerating. PR2 sets the maximum chuff or pulse rate. PR3 sets the idling speed and should be omitted if a steam chuff effect is required which must start from zero.

For a steam-outline locomotive we can arrange for automatic switching to whistle as a train-mounted reed switch passes over a track-mounted magnet. Figure 30.3 shows a circuit which sounds the whistle, interrupting the chuffs, for about 1 second.

Through-the-rails sound

In this system the sound generator IC becomes a part of the controller. In my experiments the controller was the same as that described in Chapter 27 in connection with high-frequency train lighting, except for the following differences: (i) the 'lower' power supply is stabilised at 9 V and (ii) the feedback loop bypass capacitor was increased to 100 μF so that the feedback loop no longer functioned at audio frequencies. The 94281 and its associated components now take the place of the 555 timer giving the circuit shown in Figure 30.4, which delivers pure DC with superimposed audio. The circuitry around T5 and T6 provides for the chuff or pulse rate to be synchronised (roughly) with train speed; VR2, VR3 and VR4 are analogous to PR1, PR2 and PR3 in Figure 30.2.

On board the train itself all we need, in theory, is the speaker with a blocking capacitor connected straight across the rails. The purpose of the blocking capacitor is to prevent DC from the controller from interfering with the speaker and indeed from burning it out. In practice, unfortunately, it is not as simple as that. The capacitor needs to be a high-value electrolytic type and non-polarised. These are expensive, so I used a pair of polarised types (400 μF, 40 V) 'back to back', which proved quite satisfactory. As a further precaution against damage to the speaker, I added a 6 V grain-of-wheat lamp in series with the speaker and capacitors, as shown in Figure 30.5. If the capacitors should become leaky so that controller's DC output reaches the lamp plus speaker, the lamp will light, absorbing most of the power and if the lamp should burn out, it will at least have served a useful purpose in protecting the rather more expensive speaker. In general use I have not had any failures with this circuit.

The lamp is also useful as an aid in setting the sound effect levels. A good level appears to correspond to the lamp glowing gently in time with the sound. In a steam-outline loco you might be able to use an orange-tinted lamp in the firebox which will glow prototypically in time with the chuffs.

If the sound is turned off, but the train is left running, the speaker does deliver some crackles and buzzes originating from the motor, but these are faint and are normally drowned by the mechanical sounds of the train as it runs.

Some locos will reproduce some through-the rails sounds without even needing a speaker. Best for this purpose are those fitted with the Hornby XO3/XO4-type motor or the Airfix five-pole motors. Chuffs and hisses will be reproduced faintly but audibly at low settings of the speed control; this is caused by the armature 'rattling' as the AC component of the audio signal is applied to its coils. As the loco gathers speed, however, the armature gains momentum which counteracts the reciprocating tendency, so that the sound dies away.

An interesting spin-off from through-the-rails sound is that the pure DC controller becomes compatible with live-rail track circuits. Even trains not fitted with speakers are detected normally by the live-rail track circuit provided that the sound is on. If the sound is turned off, train detection fails when the controller output is positive relative to the layout common return. Vehicles fitted with speakers and blocking capacitors are detected by track circuits in the absence of locos, provided that the sound is on. Through-the-rails sound, therefore, is compatible with all types of track circuiting, but not with speedometer circuits, nor, regrettably, with high-frequency train lighting (Chapter 27). Although the controller circuit is almost identical to that described in Chapter 27, the HF generator causes intolerable interference with the audio system. Furthermore, the audio frequencies will in certain circumstances light lamps with blocking capacitors intended for HF lighting. If you want through-the-rails sound *and* constant train lighting, you must opt for the battery-based lighting system described in Chapter 28.

General appendices

For appendices 1 and 2 see pages 37 and 55.

Appendix 3: Fault finding

So, you've built it and it doesn't work. What next? Tearing your hair or kicking the cat won't help.

How to get it right the first time

Prevention is better than cure, so let's see how to construct projects in such a way that they *do* work first time. The secret is to test everything at every stage as far as possible. Let's see how this works first for a simple project, *viz* the controller in Chapter 1.

Power Supply. You will need a power supply to run the finished controller, but it's a good idea to have it ready right at the beginning. Plug it in and switch it on. First, test its output voltage with a test meter and if that is satisfactory, put your test meter on the highest available current range (10 A is not too high) and connect it straight across the output. The meter should swing over to 1 or 2 A before the circuit breaker or current limiter comes into action. You now know that your power supply will deliver both the Volts and the Amps that your finished controller will need. This may sound trite, but it is amazing how many electronic projects have been built *correctly* but rejected as failures because they failed to work when connected to a faulty power supply.

Circuit Board. You must decide now on tag-strip, Veroboard or group board or some other means of construction. We shall use the word 'board' loosely to indicate the assembly, whatever form it takes. Provide your positive and negative input connections, choose a suitable speed control potentiometer and wire its outer terminals to the positive and negative lines. Connect the board to the power supply. Select a suitable voltage range on the test meter; connect the black probe to the negative line and the red probe to the slider of the pot. Now run the slider from minimum to maximum and back a few times watching what happens on the meter. The voltage should go up and down smoothly in unison with the movement of the slider. Again, I have seen controllers fail because the speed control pot was faulty. The carbon tracks in pots have been known to develop cracks, so the pot becomes in effect a two-position switch: with the slider below the crack the speed is zero; above the crack the speed is maximum. No wonder the circuit is rejected as a non-runner!

Select a resistor for R1 and check with the test meter that its resistance is what you think it is. Insert R1 and T1. *Temporarily* ground T1's emitter. Connect the test meter (voltage range) between T1's collector and supply positive. Now swing the speed control again. At minimum speed the meter should indicate no volts but at quite a low setting of the speed control the full supply voltage should appear as T1 goes into saturation. OK, you have a working T1. Disconnect T1's emitter from ground and insert D1. Repeat the last test. You should get no voltage reading at all — or perhaps a barely perceptible movement of the needle owing to leakage current.

Insert IC1. Connect the test meter (voltage range) across the controller output, ie across D1. Swing the speed control back and forth a few times. The results should be identical to those of the very first test when you were measuring the voltage on the slider of the pot. The circuit is, after all, a 'voltage follower'. The difference is, though the meter does not know it, that the controller will now deliver up to *n* Amps of current at any voltage you care to set when *n* is the threshold of the circuit breaker or current limiter in the power supply. If all is well, wire in the reversing switch and repeat the tests on both settings of the switch. You will need to transpose the probes when you operate the switch. If all is well, connect the controller to your railway and see how it handles a train.

If all is *not* well, by following this procedure you will at least know at what stage of construction things went wrong. Suppose, for instance, that you put in D1 the wrong way round. You would have quickly discovered that T1 was still behaving as though its emitter were grounded and, if in your haste to finish the controller and see it work, you forgot to carry out that test and proceeded to insert IC1, you would quickly discover things had run amok at the next test. Instead of following the input voltage obediently, it would follow it up to about 1 V and then the overload cutout would trip each time. The test suggests that we have a short circuit in the controller output, so we look at our output circuit and spot D1. D1 is supposed to be reverse biased, we tell ourselves, but when we look at our board we see that we have got in the wrong way round. Exactly the kind of mistake that we all make when we're anxious to complete a project and see how it performs.

What applies to simple projects applies even more to complex ones. Probably the most complex project in this book is the progressive cab control unit (Chapter 26). The first prototype was built as follows.

First, IC4 was put in with the ties and connections needed for the *second* bistable only (IC4c/d). T2 with its LED was inserted. Power was applied and the bistable checked using the test meter on a current range to momentarily ground one bistable input, then the other. The bistable worked fine. This was repeated with the other bistable (IC4a/d) and its associated circuitry. This, too, worked fine. Next, IC3 was put in. There was no easy way of testing the bistable circuitry at this stage, but the 'unconnected train' LED should have lit when power was applied. It didn't, but I decided to press on and fit IC1 before further testing. With IC1 went the advise input switches which would help considerably in later testing. At this stage pressing either 'advise' input should illuminate the appropriate 'controller connnected' LED. In practice, pressing 'advise A' brought on *both* LEDs, which correctly could be cleared using the 'isolate' switch. Pressing 'Advise B' did nothing. The 'unconnected train' LED still stubbornly refused to light under any circumstances.

An initial study of the board showed that a short circuit had joined the two transistors' collectors together. When separated, pressing the 'Advise A' button correctly brought on only the 'A connected' LED. Further examination showed a bad contact as responsible for the non-illumination of the 'unconnected train' LED, which now behaved. However, 'Advise B' still did nothing and this was worrying as both bistable circuits had worked perfectly.

At this stage I analysed the circuit using a logic probe. This is a very handy gadget which I unhesitatingly recommend to all who dabble with logic circuitry. It has two leads which are connected to the power supply of the circuit under investigation. The probe tip can be used to contact any part of the circuit. If it encounters a logical '0', one LED lights. If it encounters a logical '1' another LED lights. If it encounters an indeterminate voltage or is left open circuit, neither LED lights. It's much faster than a voltmeter because you do not have to look away from the circuit to the meter — the LEDs are at the base of the device's body — and it gives a nice 'digital' ('0' or '1') readout. The probe showed that one gate of IC4 and one gate of IC1 were not following their proper logic. IC1 was easy to check; it was in an IC socket, so out it came and in went a replacement. The performance was unchanged, suggesting that both ICs were fine; the fault was on the board. A very close scrutiny of the underside of the Veroboard, tracing the conductors away from the anomalously-behaving gates led me to the tiniest whisker of copper shorting two adjacent conductors together. With this removed, the circuit behaved perfectly, at last. IC2, IC5, IC6 and IC7 followed, fortunately without malfunction.

Faults in completed equipment

Never mind the how but you have a piece of equipment that does not work. Presumably you have a circuit diagram so reference to this should give you some idea of how much current the circuit should take from its power supply and also of what the voltages (or logic levels) should be at various points in the circuit.

First, check the current consumption. This may tell you everything or it may tell you nothing. If it is excessively high, this suggests some kind of short circuit. The affected components are likely to heat up quite quickly so that your sense of touch (and smell!) may enable you to locate them quite rapidly. If the current is too low, this suggests that the circuit, or part of it, is not making contact with the power supply. I built a radio receiver once which failed to work and which the meter told me at once was taking *no* current. The reason? I had correctly connected the earthy side of the battery to the frame of the tuning capacitor, but I had forgotten to insert a link from the said frame to the return line of the circuit! Once connected, the receiver worked perfectly. It's the real sillies like this that the current consumption test shows up. It's when the current consumption is more or less normal and the circuit still doesn't work, that the fault is more subtle and you must locate it by irregularities in the voltages or logic levels. There are a few useful 'tricks' that may help you locate a fault rapidly.

Remember that a transistor, when functioning normally, will have its base and emitter voltages 0.7 V apart. So, if you find a transistor where there is a great difference, say 3 V, between base and emitter, that transistor is suspect. The same is true for TTL gates. If you find a NAND gate with '1's on all inputs *and* on its output, something is very wrong. That is not to say that that gate has most definitely failed. It could be, for instance, that a solder blob or copper whisker is short circuiting its output terminal to supply positive.

These checks do not tell you *what* is wrong, but they help you to find *where* something is wrong. To spot what is actually causing the malfunction may still involve some tracing along the conductors. Never be afraid to search.

Kinds of faults

Let us now have a look at the kind of fault that we are likely to discover at the end of our quest.

Component failure is, in my experience, very rare. Most modern components are well tested before despatch and remain serviceable even if subject to considerable abuse.

Component wrongly inserted. The correct component has been used but with its leads interchanged, eg base and emitter interchanged. Watch out for this with transistors having unusual pin-outs, eg some variants of the BC182/ 212 family. Also watch out for the pin-out of the 7402 (74LS02) IC which is different from all other two-input gates (except the rarely used '01).

Wrong component. When the switching regulator for the battery-back-up train lighting system (Chapter 28) was first finished, it failed to work. The output transistor delivered the full input voltage and several components got very hot. I checked all connections and all were correct. Then I spotted that T2 was a BC557 (pnp) where the circuit demanded a BC547 (npn)! Substitution of the correct transistor made the circuit work. This kind of error is very easy to make especially where a one-digit difference in the component type number may make a world of difference to performance. Watch out for a similar problem with resistors. I have seen resistors apparently coded brown/black/ brown (100 Ω) but with a barely perceptible difference in hue between the two brown bands. In fact the third band was supposed to be orange and the resistor was 10 K. Another common resistor error is to select brown/red/black (12 Ω) thinking you have brown/black/red (1 K). *Always* before using a resistor check it on the meter. You will be amazed at what you think is something else!

Bad contacts. These are normally the results of bad soldering. The joint may *look* fine and may even function properly for a while, but there is no fixed metal-to-metal contact and one day physical stress on one side of the joint causes the component to move and electrical contact is lost.

Circuit board faults. Nearly all of my circuits nowadays use Veroboard, an excellent medium and ideal for use with ICs but Veroboard lays the unwary constructor open to two faults, both very common. Firstly, when making a break in a conductor by means of a spot face cutter (stripboard cutter) make absolutely certain that you have fully separated the two parts of the conductor. It is easy to leave an almost microscopic trace of copper around the edge of the hole. Examine your break very carefully under a powerful light and don't feel a fool in checking the continuity (or rather, discontinuity) with the meter. Better to make certain now rather than waste hours later on looking for an elusive short circuit in the finished project. Secondly, it sometimes happens that the slivers of copper that result from the use of the spot face cutter come to rest so that they are shorting two conductors. They are very small, so easily go unnoticed. Molten flux from later soldering operations can even 'glue' such slivers into permanent short circuits (as on my prototype progressive cab control unit). The only evidence will be two adjacent conductors always at the same voltage. You must search diligently under a powerful lamp and a magnifying glass. The offending sliver, when located, can be hacked out using the blade of a miniature screwdriver. In fact, it is not a bad idea to score along between the conductors of a finished circuit board in the hope of breaking any such particles.

All that has been said above about copper particles applies equally to solder blobs which can also cause some hard-to-locate and harder-to-remove short circuits between conductors.

Conclusion

It has not been possible to give anything more than general hints, since every circuit and every method of construction has its own peculiar traps for the unwary. Yet I hope that I have encouraged you to look analytically at your failed project rather than throw it out of the window!

Appendix 4: Transistor/transistor logic (TTL)

Many domestic and industrial appliances now demand for their operation the ability to 'reason', albeit on a minor scale. Examples range from automatic washing machines offering a range of 'programmes' through automobile electrical systems to video games. These items and many more make use of the 'families' of electronic logic ICs now available. These ICs contain transistors (MOSFETs in CMOS logic) configured to perform various logic functions that will be described later.

These ICs are ideal for use in automatic signalling systems and certain other model railway equipment which is fundamentally 'logical' in its operation. This is why Parts 3 and 4 of this book bristle with them.

A consequence of the very widespread use of this technology is that the ICs are universally available and very cheap. One supplier's catalogue drawn at random quotes the BC108B, the archetypal silicon npn small-signal transistor, at 10p but the 74LS00 quad two-input NAND gate (the archetypal TTL IC) at 9p and this contains the equivalent of 20 transistors!

Logic families

There are several 'families' of transistor/transistor logic (TTL) devices. Best known is the 74 series having four- or five-digit numbers beginning with 74, eg 7400, 7408, 74157. These are now officially obsolete, but are still widely available. Current 'industry standard' is the 74LS series, whose numbering and pin-out is in general the same as the 74 series, but the letters LS are inserted after the 74, eg 74LS00, 74LS08, 74LS157. The LS stands for low-power Schottky and this series is characterised by being more miserly on current than the older 74 series.

The 74LS is in turn being replaced by the 74ALS series (advanced low-power Schottky) offering further improvement, which will one day be the industry standard. At the time of writing, however, 74ALS devices are only beginning to make their appearance. With certain limitations (explained later under the heading 'Fan out') 74 and 74LS ICs can be used interchangeably, although I recommend that, as far as possible, you should stick to one family or the other, 74LS being preferable. Wherever in this book a 74 series is specified, use the 74LS equivalent if possible.

Another widely used family is CMOS logic. The devices have four- or five-digit numbers beginning with 4, eg 4007, 4029. Although CMOS is flexible in its power supply requirements (3 V to 18 V), its use is not recommended because certain precautions must be taken to avoid accidental damage to the MOSFETs of which the logic circuits are composed. Furthermore, the output current available from most CMOS devices is very limited, often less than 1 mA. So you cannot normally drive LEDs direct from CMOS outputs as you can from 74 or 74LS outputs.

Other logic families you are less likely to encounter are ECL (emitter-coupled logic), 74C (CMOS with pin-outs as 74 series), 74S (Schottky) and 74L (low power).

Power requirements

The 74 and 74LS devices require what to railway modellers is the slightly awkward 5 V DC smoothed *and stabilised* supply. The easiest way to provide this is to take an unstabilised but smoothed supply delivering 7 V to 12 V and feed this through a 7805 (or similar) 5 V regulator (see Figure A4.1). The 7805 will deliver up to 1 A with very accurate regulation. *On no account should you attempt to operate TTL from any kind of unstabilised power supply.*

All your TTL devices may share the power supply. You are recommended to

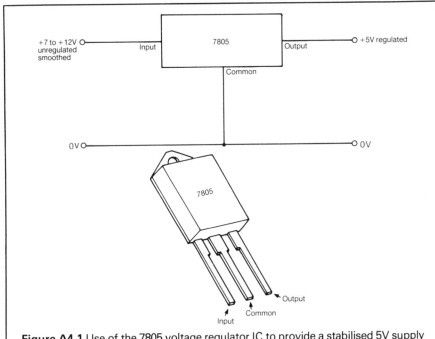

Figure A4.1 Use of the 7805 voltage regulator IC to provide a stabilised 5V supply for TTL. The 7805 should be bolted to a heat sink if the total dissipation $\dfrac{(V_{in} - V_{out})}{I}$ exceeds 1 W.

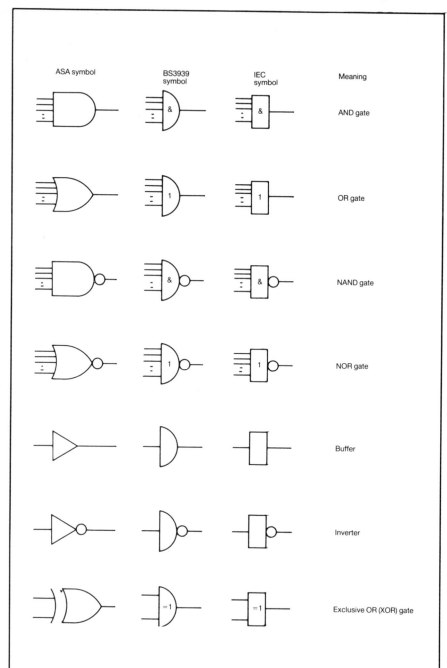

Figure A4.2 Symbols for logic gates.

include 0.1 μF smoothing capacitors from supply positive to ground at intervals through your circuitry, about one capacitor for every five ICs.

Logic levels

The active devices in the 74 and 74LS ICs are bipolar transistors. In logic circuitry these transistors are used as switches only. Consequently each transistor is either fully 'on', ie saturated or near saturation in the 74LS series, or it is 'off', ie not conducting. So inputs to and outputs from the ICs are either *high* or *low*. A high output is typically 2.4 V or higher while low output is typically 0.4 V or below. The maximum input that a device will read as low is 0.8 V and the minimum output that a device will read as high is 2.0 V.

A high input or output is often called a logical '1' and a low input or output is often called a logical '0'. These '1's and '0's are often collectively called *data,* a plural word of which the singular is *datum.* They are called *data* because they convey useful information which the whole logic circuit processes. For example, a '0' from a track circuit output may indicate 'train in section' which we feed into a signalling system; this processes the data and acts upon it by illuminating the appropriate signal aspects. The smallest unit of data, ie a single 'slot' which may be (indeed *must* be) occupied by a '0' or a '1', is called a *bit,* short for *binary digit.*

The simplest TTL devices, and those of most immediate use in model railway electronics, are known as *gates.*

Gates

A *gate* in logic circuitry is a device having a number (often 1, 2, 3 or 4) of identical inputs and one output. The logic level on the output is determined by the combination of levels on the inputs.

There are three basic types of gates and others that are combinations of the basic three. The basic three are called AND, OR and NOT gates. Each is recognised by its own symbol. (Actually a profusion of different symbols are used — see Figures A4.2 and A4.4 — of which the American Standard symbols are in most general use and these are used throughout this book. The AND and OR symbols are used apart from electronics, eg in critical path analysis.) These symbols are used in circuit diagrams as though each gate were a single component. This is just a 'shorthand' to save drawing out the complete internal circuit for the gate; we shall look at the internal circuitry of some gates later on (Figures A4.5 and A4.6).

An AND gate is a gate having two or more inputs which gives a '1' output only when there is a '1' on *every* input, ie on input 1 AND input 2 AND input 3 AND *ad infinitum.* A corollary of this is that, if there is a '0' on *any* input, the output is '0'.

An OR gate is a gate having two or more inputs which gives a '1' output if there is a '1' on any input or inputs, ie on input 1 OR input 2 OR input 3 OR *ad infinitum.* So, it follows that the output is '0' only if there is a '0' on *every* input.

A NOT gate is more commonly known as an *inverter.* It has only one input and the output is the complement of the input. That is to say, if the input is '0', the output is '1'. And if the input is '1', the output is '0'. The output is whichever the input is NOT.

Three very commonly used gates are combinations of these three basic gates:

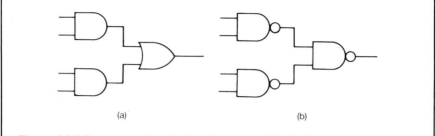

(a)   (b)

Figure A4.3 Two ways of achieving the same AND-OR function.

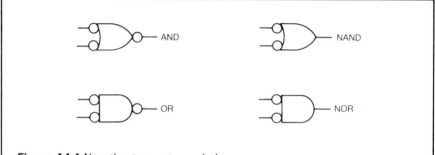

Figure A4.4 Negative-true gate symbols.

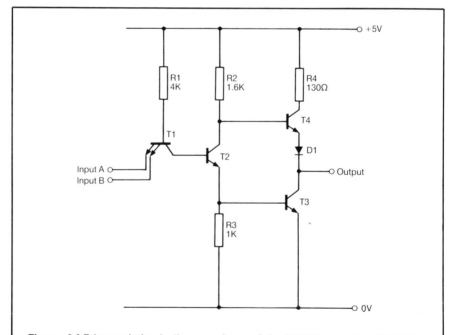

Figure A4.5 Internal circuit diagram of one of the NAND gates in a 7400 IC.

the NAND gate, the NOR gate and the exclusive OR (XOR) gate. A NAND (NOT AND) gate is an AND gate incorporating an inverter before its output terminal. So, if there is a '1' on every input, the output will be '0'. And if there is a '0' on any input, the output will be '1'. Similarly a NOR (NOT OR) gate is an OR gate having an inverter before its output terminal. So a '1' on any input will give a '0' on the output. And when there is a '0' on every input there will be a '1' on the output. An exclusive OR (XOR) gate is a variant of the OR gate. It is a two-input gate in which a '1' on one input *but not both* gives a '1' output. It gives a '0' output if both inputs are '0's or both '1's. You could say that it gives a '0' output if the inputs are similar and a '1' if they are dissimilar. There is also a version which has an inverter before its output and is known as an exclusive NOR (XNOR) gate.

Generally the inverting gates (NAND and NOR) are more useful than the non-inverting gates (AND and OR). NAND, NOR and AND gates are all available with 2, 3 or 4 inputs, some with more. OR gates are only available with 2 inputs.

It may seem that the OR gate gets a raw deal, but there are other ways of achieving the OR function, as we shall see.

De Morgan's Theorem
If you look again at the description of the gate types given above, you will see that there are two ways in which each gate can be used. The AND gate, for instance, only behaves as an AND gate when we are considering inputs that are '1's, that is to say, when we are using *positive-true* logic. Alternatively, we could decide that the inputs in which we are interested are '0's (as indeed we do in the signal driver circuits in Chapter 12). This is called *negative-true* logic. Inputs or outputs which are negative true are designated either by a bar over the name, eg section occupied, or a prime (') after the name, eg advise A'.

Now, if the data that we are processing consist of '0's, we find that the gates behave differently. For instance, to quote what I said about AND gates earlier, 'if there is a "0" on any input, the output is "0"'. Thus our AND gate behaves as though it were an OR gate when dealing with '0's, which is how AND gates are used in Chapters 13, 14 and 15. Indeed, in general, if you use negative-true logic, an AND gate behaves as an OR gate, an OR gate behaves as an AND gate, a NAND gate behaves as a NOR gate and a NOR gate behaves as a NAND gate. This is the basis of what is called *De Morgan's Theorem*.

You do not have to stick to one convention (positive-true or negative-true) throughout one circuit; you can mix them. Indeed, there is a lot to be said for mixing them. If you use inverting gates, you change convention at every stage. This permits much greater flexibility and therefore economy in the selection of your gates. For example, in the progressive cab control unit (Chapter 26) there is a function as follows: we want a '1' output (to activate the interlock) if the train is moving forwards *and* the next section is unavailable *or* if the train is moving backwards *and* the previous section is unavailable. The inputs are all '1's, so at first thought the obvious arrangement is two ANDs feeding an OR as in Figure A4.3(a). However, we do not use AND or OR gates anywhere else in this unit and it would be wasteful to specify a 7408 (quad AND) and a 7432 (quad OR) and then to leave five of the eight gates unused, even if the two ICs together do cost only 40p. If you examine the circuit of the three-controller version, you will see a most elegant alternative arrangement reproduced in Figure A4.3(b). Two NAND gates provide the AND function, but their outputs are inverted of course. However, since the OR function is being applied to '0's, by De Morgan we now need an AND gate and because we want to invert its output back to a '1', it is in fact a further NAND gate that we choose. The three NAND gates are identical and indeed are on the same 7400 IC.

So important is De Morgan's Theorem that many authors use a second set of graphic symbols for the various gate types when their inputs are negative-true. These are shown in Figure A4.4 and they reflect the *function* that the gate is fulfilling rather than the name by which you would ask for it in a shop. However, throughout this book, for simplicity, only the positive-true symbols are used, whether the logic is positive-true or negative-true. I take the view that where the circuit diagram shows a NAND gate, that is what you must order from your supplier, whether it is being used as a NAND or a NOR or even, as often happens, as an inverter.

Using the gates

Figure A4.5 shows the internal circuit diagram of one of the four two-input NAND gates in a 7400 IC. The gates in the 74LS00 are rather different, as we shall see shortly. All the devices in the 74 family have similar input arrangements and most have similar output facilities. Exceptions to the latter are units having open-collector output and three-state output, which we shall consider later (under the heading 'Fan in').

Transistor T1 is a transistor with two emitters. In discrete components transistors having more than one emitter are rare, although they do exist. In fact there is no limit to the number of emitters a transistor could have. Our two-emitter transistor is perhaps best considered as two separate conventional transistors having their bases and collectors connected in parallel.

Here's how the NAND gate works. If both inputs are held high or left unconnected, no emitter current can flow. So T1's base/collector junction is *forward biased,* providing base bias for T2, whose emitter current in turn provides bias for T3, which conducts, holding the output low; because T2 is saturated, T4's base voltage is held low, barely above T3's base voltage. Now D1 pushes T4's emitter voltage higher than its base voltage, so T4 is cut off. The output of the gate is therefore low, a logical '0'. Yet, if a low voltage is applied to either input, or both, T1 functions as an ordinary transistor under saturation conditions. Its collector voltage falls almost to the low input voltage, so T2 and, in turn, T3 are cut off. Resistor R3 now provides base bias for T4 which conducts, delivering (via D1) a high voltage at the output, a logical '1'.

Figure A4.6 shows the circuit of a NAND gate in a 74LS00 IC. The principal differences between this and a 7400 NAND gate are: (i) that the input is provided by a matrix of Schottky diodes; (ii) that the transistors are all Schottky transistors and (iii) that the resistor values are generally higher than in the 7400, reducing all the current flows.

Note the different symbols used to distinguish Schottky diodes and transistors. Schottky diodes use a mixture of metal (often aluminium) and semiconductor in their junctions, which gives them a lower forward voltage, typically less than 0.2 V, compared with 0.6 to 0.7 V for a normal silicon diode. Consequently Schottky diodes are ideally suited for use in logic circuits.

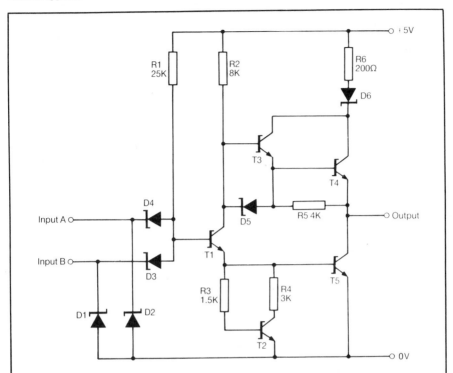

Figure A4.6 Internal circuit diagram of one of the NAND gates in a 74LS00 IC. Note the special symbols used for Schottky diodes and transistors (explained in the text).

Schottky *transistors* are ordinary silicon transistors, which incorporate a Schottky diode parallel to their base/collector junctions (cathode to the collector of an npn transistor). The function of this diode is to prevent the transistor from becoming fully saturated. As the saturation point is approached, the diode comes into conduction, short-circuiting away the excess base bias. The reason for the undesirability of saturation is that it affects the speed at which a transistor can respond to a change of bias. A saturated transistor takes longer to turn off than a transistor that is held just short of saturation by a Schottky diode. The difference is a fraction of a microsecond, irrelevant in the average model railway application, but it makes an appreciable difference to the speed at which gates can be switched in high-speed computing applications. So Schottky logic can work faster than 'plain' 74-series TTL.

A consequence of this kind of circuitry is that the input to a TTL device, 74 series or 74LS, *sources* current; it never sinks it. When an input is high, *no current flows* and when an input is low, *current flows out of it*. Experienced designers unfamiliar with the peculiarities of TTL have been baffled by its input characteristics and projects have failed when their designers have mistakenly expected current to flow *into* inputs at logical '1', as it would if the input were to the base of an npn transistor. This arrangement was chosen

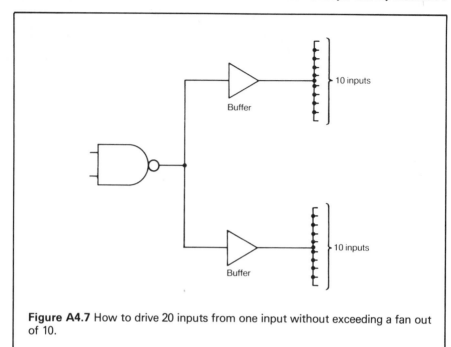

Figure A4.7 How to drive 20 inputs from one input without exceeding a fan out of 10.

because it gives TTL considerable immunity to noise and other electrical interference. It is also easier to analyse circuitry when the difference between '0' and '1' is 2.4 V or so, rather than only 0.7 V as it would be if the input were to the base of an npn transistor.

You may wonder why, having this kind of input arrangement, it was considered necessary for TTL to be given a push-pull-type output which can source or sink current. In fact it is not necessary. Open-collector versions are available (see later under 'Fan in') in which the output transistor equivalent to T4 in Figure A4.5 (or T5 in Figure A4.6) is omitted. This type of output can only sink current when in the low state; it cannot source current in the high state. For some applications these units can be used interchangeably with the normal push-pull output types. Yet TTL is sometimes used at high frequencies (up to 45 MHz), although not normally so in model railway applications. At such high frequencies the internal capacitance of the devices has a significant effect upon their efficiency of operation and a push-pull-type output allows more rapid charge and discharge of the internal capacitance, so that it can work faster.

From the railway modeller's viewpoint, speed of operation is generally irrelevant, as a response time in milliseconds would be adequate but the push-pull type output is useful in allowing the driving of common-anode or common-cathode LEDs.

Typical total input current for 74 series is 1 mA and for 74LS series is 200 μA; typical maximum output current to ground with output high is 20 mA for 74 series (10 mA for 74LS) and to supply positive when at logical '0' is about 55 mA (28 mA for 74LS).

Fan out

TTL devices are so designed that the output of one device can be connected directly to the input(s) of other device(s) without need for any intermediary components. This greatly simplifies circuit design and construction. There is, however, a limit to the number of inputs that can be serviced from one output. This figure is called the *fan out*. For a circuit consistently using 74 series, fan out is quoted as 10. That is to say, one output can feed up to 10 inputs. For 74LS, fan out is quoted as 20 and if you mix 74 and 74LS, you must allow for the differences between them. So if a 74 output is feeding 74LS inputs, fan out rises to 40 to 50 and for a 74LS output feeding 74 inputs, fan out falls to 5.

There may be occasions (although none occurs in any of the circuits described in this book) when you need to feed more inputs than the fan out permits, eg 20 inputs from one output (assuming consistent use of the 74 series). The solution is to use intermediary *buffers* (not the railway type!). These are TTL gates having one input and one output in which the output simply 'follows' the input, '0' for '0' and '1' for '1'. We can now connect two buffer inputs to our 'feeder' output and 10 inputs to each buffer output (Figure A4.7).

If you do exceed the fan out, you may find that the driving device cannot handle the output current and gives indeterminate outputs, eg its '1's are too low and some receiving devices read them as '0's or its '0's are too high and some receiving devices read them as '1's. So beware! Those who break the rules of the game are liable to incur penalties.

Fan in

The *fan in* of a TTL device is the number of other devices which may feed data directly into it. Normally this is the same as its number of inputs, eg a four-input NAND gate (on the 7420 IC) may receive inputs from each of four other gates, one output to each input. Therefore it has a fan in of four.

Although one output may feed several inputs (fan out), great care must be taken if more than one output is connected to the same input terminal. An electrical problem is liable to arise if you connect two normal (push-pull) TTL outputs in parallel. All is fine as long as both outputs agree and deliver the same logic level, but if they disagree, one will short-circuit the other, leading to an indeterminate reading. There are three ways of overcoming this problem: (i) avoid the problem altogether by using an additional AND or OR gate to perform this combining function; (ii) the use of open-collector devices and (iii) the use of three-state devices.

Open-collector devices have already been mentioned. These do not have the normal push-pull output; the output is the open collector of T3 in Figure A4.5 or of T4 in Figure A4.6, the upper output transistor having been removed. Many TTL gates, buffers and inverters are available with open-collector outputs. In this book and in some other publications an open-collector output is distinguished in circuit diagrams by an asterisk adjacent to the output terminal.

Open-collector outputs may be connected in parallel, whereupon a '0' on *any* output will be read as a '0' by any input(s) connected to this point. Only if all the outputs are at '1', ie non-conductive, will the input(s) read a '1'. Therefore, this arrangement behaves as though it were an AND gate; sometimes it is called a 'wired AND', or a 'wired OR', because most often it is handling negative-true logic in which, by De Morgan's Theorem, AND behaves as OR.

Several examples of open-collector NAND gates are used in the progressive cab control modules described in Chapter 26. For example, all the 'advise' outputs are from this type of device because they are likely to be paralleled or short-circuited in normal use.

It is recommended that open-collector outputs be equipped with a pull-up resistor (1 K to 10 K) to supply positive. Its function is to pull the output up to the logic '1' level when the output transistors are off. Although in theory the circuit should work without the pull-up resistor, in the electrically noisy environment of a working model railway, its inclusion will help to eliminate interference.

Three-state devices sound as though they employ a third logic level in addition to '0' and '1', but the truth is simpler. They have a push-pull-type output, but both output transistors are normally open-circuit, so that neither a '0' nor a '1' is delivered. These devices incorporate a separate 'enable' input, to which a '1' in some devices or a '0' in other devices must be applied to activate the output stage and enable the output data to be read. Consequently any number of three-state outputs may be connected in parallel, provided that no more than one at a time is enabled. Only the selected and enabled (the proper term is 'addressed') device's output will be read by any inputs connected to the common data line (the proper term is 'bus'). The system functions somewhat like a data selector (see below). The number of three-state devices is limited and there are probably not many occasions on which their characteristics are likely to render them useful to railway modellers.

Data selectors (Multiplexers)

Some of the most useful 'gate variants' in model railway electronics are the data selectors, sometimes called multiplexers. One example, the 74LS157 is put to good model railway use in Chapter 18. As the name suggests, these devices select logical data from a choice of sources. The 74LS157 is a quad two-input selector; that is to say, it functions rather like a four-pole two-way switch, except that it is only *inputs* that are selected. It cannot be used (as a two-way switch can) to *distribute* data to selected receivers, which is the function of a *demultiplexer*. The 74LS157 is ideally suited for switching the inputs to a multiple-aspect signal driver at a running junction; which is how it is used in Chapter 18. A functional diagram of the 74LS157 is given in Figure A4.8.

Other multiplexers in common use are the 74LS151 (single 8-input), 74LS153 (dual 4-input) and the 74LS158 (as the '157 but with inverted outputs). A useful feature on all these devices is their enable input. If a logical '1' is applied to this input, all the outputs go to '0', irrespective of the other inputs. So normally this input is kept 'low'. In Figure 18.5 you will see it used to provide a manual over-ride for the signal.

Demultiplexers and decoders

The 'opposite' of a data selector or multiplexer is called a *demultiplexer* or sometimes, incorrectly, a *decoder*. It has an input terminal, an array of output terminals and one or more address terminals. The input data are transmitted exclusively to the output terminal selected by the code applied to the address terminals.

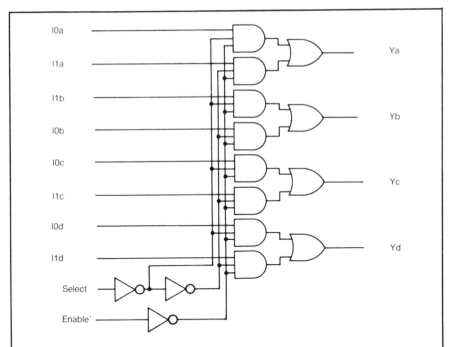

Figure A4.8 Functional diagram of the '157 quad two-input data selector (multiplexer).

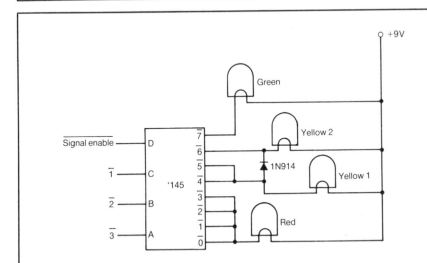

Figure A4.9 A BCD-to-decimal decoder used as a four-aspect signal driver for a signal using grain-of-wheat bulbs. It could equally well use LEDs. The signal enable input could be used to provide flashing aspects. The decoder IC, of course, needs a standard 5 V TTl supply.

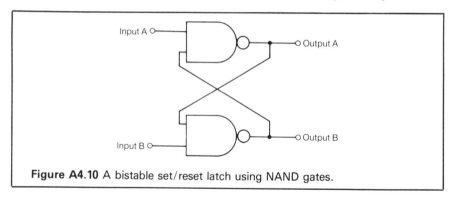

Figure A4.10 A bistable set/reset latch using NAND gates.

A *decoder,* when correctly used, is similar to a demultiplexer, but lacks the input terminal. It simply has address inputs and outputs. Two of the best known TTL decoders, a pair of extraordinarily useful ICs, are the 7442 and 74145 (74LS42 and 74LS145) binary-code-decimal (BCD) to decimal decoders. These are 16-pin ICs with four address inputs called D, C, B and A and ten outputs numbered $\bar{0}$ to $\bar{9}$. Each of the ten outputs is addressed by a unique combination of address inputs designed to perform the arithmetical function of BCD to decimal conversion. The one addressed output is a logical '0' while all others are '1'. If the input code has a decimal value exceeding 9, *all* outputs are '1's. The following table shows the behaviour of these decoders.

Input DCBA	Output	Input DCBA	Output
0 0 0 0	$\bar{0}$ low; others high	1 0 0 0	$\bar{8}$ low; others high
0 0 0 1	$\bar{1}$ low; others high	1 0 0 1	$\bar{9}$ low; others high
0 0 1 0	$\bar{2}$ low; others high	1 0 1 0	all high
0 0 1 1	$\bar{3}$ low; others high	1 0 1 1	all high
0 1 0 0	$\bar{4}$ low; others high	1 1 0 0	all high
0 1 0 1	$\bar{5}$ low; others high	1 1 0 1	all high
0 1 1 0	$\bar{6}$ low; others high	1 1 1 0	all high
0 1 1 1	$\bar{7}$ low; others high	1 1 1 1	all high

Although these ICs may have been intended originally for arithmetical functions, their applications are far broader. They may be regarded as 'universal three or four input gates'. Suppose we want to identify those situations in which the logic levels at three points are 1, 1 and 1 respectively and we want a logical '0' output. This is easy: we use a three-input NAND gate with inputs from those points. However, suppose the three levels are 1, 1 and 0. We could apply an inverter to the third point and still use the three-input NAND. We might just happen to have a spare inverter somewhere, or a spare NAND that could be used as one, or we might not, but we *could* use a '42 instead. We apply the 1, 1 and 0 points to inputs C, B and A respectively and tie input D to ground. Now 110 is BCD for 6, so we take our output from output 6. Then suppose we also need to identify those situations when the same points are at 1, 0 and 1 respectively. 101 is $\bar{5}$, so we take the new output from output 5. Any of the eight possible combinations of three inputs A, B and C can be detected in this way, provided input D is tied to ground. Many combinations of *four* inputs can be handled, provided that input D is wanted as a '0', unless it happens to form part of the two valid input codes in which it is high, ie 1000 (= 8) and 1001 (= 9).

The '145 is an interesting IC. It has the same pin-out and functions as the '42 but the outputs are open-collector type and rated to carry up to 80 mA and tolerate up to 15 V. Thus it is ideal for driving relays or grain-of-wheat bulbs. Equally valid outputs can be paralleled and this enables such fascinating circuits to be made up as the four-aspect signal driver shown in Figure A4.9.

Combinational and sequential logic

All the logic circuitry considered so far in this Appendix — and indeed most of the logic circuitry in this book — involves what is called *combinational* logic. That is logic in which the output is dependent only on the inputs being applied at that time, so that, if the status of all the inputs is known, the output can be deduced. Gates and multiplexers are examples of combinational-logic devices and the signal driver circuits in Chapter 12 (which, after all, are only combinations of gates) are examples of whole circuits displaying combinational logic.

A further dimension is added to logic circuitry by the use of *sequential logic*. This is logic circuitry in which the output is determined not only by the status of the inputs currently being applied, but also by past inputs which have subsequently disappeared. In other words, it is circuitry which has *memory*.

Consider the simple circuit shown in Figure A4.10. The two NAND gates may well be on the same 7400 IC. If we apply '0's to both inputs, we can predict the outputs; both will be '1's, since a '0' applied to any input of a NAND gate will always ensure a '1' output. Yet, what if both inputs are '1's? We can no longer predict the output, for there are two possibilities. *Either* output B will be 'high' and (since both inputs of IC1a are 'high') output A will be 'low' (holding output B 'high'), *or* output A will be 'high' and (since both inputs of IC1b are 'high') output B will be 'low' (holding output A 'high'). So both states are inherently *stable*. That is to say, the circuit if left alone will stay in the same state. This kind of circuit is called a *bistable* (or 'flip-flop'). (In *Practical Electronics for Railway Modellers* bistables composed of pairs of discrete transistors are described.)

The useful feature of this kind of bistable is that we can force it into whichever state we choose — and it will, of course, stay in that state until we decide to force it into the other state. In Figure A4.10, if we apply a '0' to input A, that gate's output will go high, so that IC1b will now have '1's on *both* inputs. Its output now goes low, holding the other input of IC1a low and this state will be maintained if we let input A return to '1'. If we now apply a '0' to input B, the bistable will go into its other state — and that similarly will be maintained until input A is activated again.

The two inputs of this bistable are often called the $\overline{\text{set}}$ and $\overline{\text{reset}}$ ($\overline{\text{S}}$ and $\overline{\text{R}}$) inputs. Since the circuit, at least in the form in which it is shown in Figure A4.10, is symmetrical it might appear to be an arbitrary decision which input is $\overline{\text{S}}$ and which is $\overline{\text{R}}$. When the bistable is used as a part of a functional system, however, it is usually obvious which is which: the $\overline{\text{S}}$ input initiates the *active* state, eg section occupied, flashing yellow aspects on, controller A engaged.

Notice that the two outputs of this bistable are antiphase. That is to say, *in normal use* one is always at '0' and the other is at '1'. This must be so, since

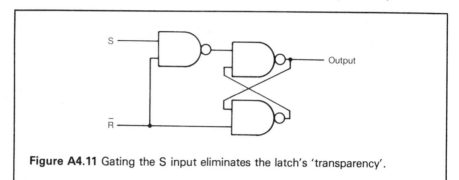

Figure A4.11 Gating the S input eliminates the latch's 'transparency'.

each output is also an input to the other gate; the output that is at '0' will cause a '1' to be delivered at the other output. Often, however, only one output is used — the one that gives a '1' output when the $\overline{S}$ input has been activated. There are TTL ICs containing arrays of such bistables, generally having a single output and often sharing a common reset input.

There is a drawback to this kind of bistable. As mentioned earlier, if a '0' is applied to both inputs simultaneously, a '1' will appear on *both* outputs. This is the one exception to the rule given in the last paragraph that in normal use the outputs are antiphase. So, in a device having a single output, even if the $\overline{R}$ input is being held at a steady '0', a '0' on the $\overline{S}$ input will give a '1' on the output. Because the output can 'see' the input in this way, this kind of bistable is sometimes called a 'transparent latch'.

This 'transparency' can be eliminated by gating the S input, ie feeding the input through a gate which is disabled by a '0' on the $\overline{R}$ input. Figure A4.11 shows one way of doing this; a similar arrangement is used in the progressive cab control units described in Chapter 26. Note that the S input is now positive-true.

There are, however, various more sophisticated bistable types which eliminate the 'transparency' problems by various means. Generally these units have an additional input called the 'clock' input to which a train of pulses is applied; these lock pulses enable changes of state. Examples are the D-type and JK bistables, both of which are widely used in electronics. Further details of their construction and use will be found in textbooks of digital electronics.

Interfacing TTL with other systems

Care must be taken when interfacing TTL to switches or other electronic circuits because of its input characteristics. Switch contacts should always be connected between the ground (supply negative line) and the TTL device input, so that the closing of the contacts is read as a logical '0'. A pull-up resistor (1 K to 10 K) should always be provided from the gate input to supply positive; its omission would render the TTL system susceptible to noise and spurious activation. See Figure A4.12. In the same way an npn transistor in place of the switch contacts is particularly useful in interfacing TTL to other electronic circuits, especially if these operate from a different supply voltage. This is shown in Figure A4.13.

Another method of using a transistor as an interface is shown in Figure A4.14. Although this configuration is possible, that of Figure A4.13 is preferable for a number of reasons. For example Rc must be a low value to sink the TTL input current: recommended maximum values are 470 Ω with 74 series and 2.2 K with 74LS. These low values, especially with 'plain' 74 series lead to heavy current consumption when the transistor is conductive.

TTL outputs are more flexible. The standard push-pull outputs can source or sink current up to 10 mA or more. LEDs can be driven direct in either mode. Auxiliary transistors or Darlingtons should be used where higher output currents or voltages or both are needed, eg for relay driving.

Some TTL ICs are available with outputs rated for heavier duties. Examples are the 74LS37 and 74LS38. Both are quad two-input NAND gates which can handle up to 50 mA of output current; the '38 has open-collector output. They are intended for applications where they are called upon to drive large numbers of other TTL inputs exceeding the normal fan out, but can also be used for other applications, eg grain-of-wheat lamp driving, provided that the output voltage limit (about 7 V) is not exceeded.

Handling TTL devices

Most common TTL ICs come in 14-pin DIL (dual-in-line) plastic packages. Pin 14 is generally supply positive and pin 7 supply negative. This leaves 12 pins for inputs and outputs. Consequently the number of gates per chip is generally as follows:

1-input gates (buffers and inverters): 6 per chip
2-input gates   4 per chip
3-input gates   3 per chip
4-input gates   2 per chip
8-input gates   1 per chip

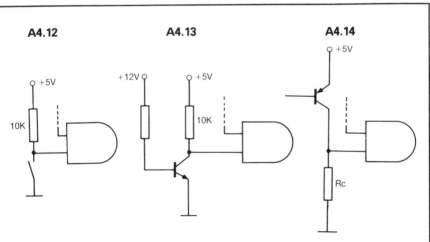

Figure A4.12 Switched inputs to TTL should be between input and ground and should include a pull-up resistor.

Figure A4.13 An npn transistor used as an interface to a TTL system.

Figure A4.14 An alternative system of using a transistor to interface to TTL. This system is less satisfactory than that of Figure A4.13 for reasons given in the text.

Due to the positions of the positive and negative supply pins, the gate connections are generally staggered, so that the output of one gate is invariably opposite the input of another. This is often very useful when constructing circuits on Veroboard or similar stripboard, since one gate can be made to feed another of the same type by simply leaving the strip intact between the pins.

Devising the simplest Veroboard arrangement for complex TTL circuits is a gruelling task. Perhaps one day someone will invent a computer program to do this!

TTL ICs are, in general, robust, trouble free and they will withstand considerable misuse. On one occasion a circuit of mine that had begun malfunctioning proved to have been hooked up to the *input* of its supply voltage regulator, so was being operated from 7.5 V unregulated. When restored to its correct supply voltage, the circuit functioned normally again, so no damage had been done. On another occasion an IC was grossly overheated when it took 30 minutes to remove a particularly stubborn solder blob that was shorting adjacent Veroboard conductors. For several minutes the IC package itself was too hot to handle but it still performed perfectly afterwards. Nevertheless, as with all ICs, I recommend the use of IC sockets. These should be soldered in place at the same time as the passive components; afterwards the ICs themselves can be inserted (a fiddly job). This not only protects the ICs against overheating when soldering (however unlikely this may be to actually cause damage) but also offers the facility for swopping ICs. In the unlikely event of the project not working (most TTL projects work perfectly first time) and of your suspecting the IC of being less than perfect, you can easily take it out and try another.

Pin-outs

On the following pages are pin-out diagrams of some of the most popular TTL ICs, including all those mentioned in this book. Note that the diagrams are all *top views*. The drawings are reproduced from the Maplin catalogue by kind permission of Maplin Electronic Supplies Ltd.

Table A4.1: Gate selector guide

NB Numbers must be prefixed 74 or 74LS etc.

AND gates	Normal output	Open-collector output	Special
Quad 2-input	08	09	—
Triple 3-input	11	15	—
Dual 4-input	21	—	—
OR gates			
Quad 2-input	32	—	—
NAND gates			
Quad 2-input	00	01	26*h**
		03	37*b*
			38*b**
			132*s*
Triple 3-input	10	12	—
Dual 4-input	20	22	13*s*

Single 8-input NOR gates	30	—	—
Quad 2-input	02	33*b*	28*b*
Triple 3-input	27	—	—
Dual 4-input XOR gates	25*a*	—	—
Quad XNOR gates	86	136	—
Quad Buffers	—	266	—
Hex Inverters (NOT)	—	07	17*h**
Hex	04	05	06*b** 14*s* 16*h**

Notes

* = open-collector output; *a* also has strobe inputs; *b* buffer output (has higher than normal current handling capacity); *h* high-voltage tolerance; *s* Schmitt trigger

Semiconductors

Reprinted by permission of Maplin Electronic Supplies Ltd.

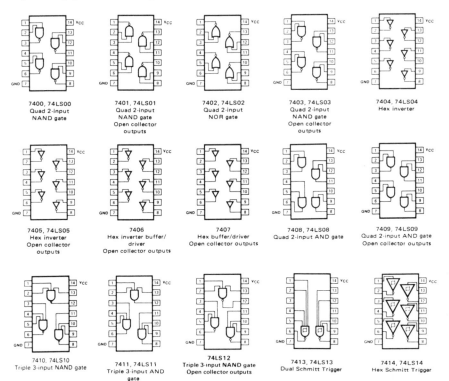

7400, 74LS00
Quad 2-input
NAND gate

7401, 74LS01
Quad 2-input
NAND gate
Open collector
outputs

7402, 74LS02
Quad 2-input
NOR gate

7403, 74LS03
Quad 2-input
NAND gate
Open collector
outputs

7404, 74LS04
Hex inverter

7405, 74LS05
Hex inverter
Open collector
outputs

7406
Hex inverter buffer/
driver
Open collector outputs

7407
Hex buffer/driver
Open collector outputs

7408, 74LS08
Quad 2-input AND gate

7409, 74LS09
Quad 2-input AND gate
Open collector outputs

7410, 74LS10
Triple 3-input NAND gate

7411, 74LS11
Triple 3-input AND
gate

74LS12
Triple 3-input NAND gate
Open collector outputs

7413, 74LS13
Dual Schmitt Trigger

7414, 74LS14
Hex Schmitt Trigger

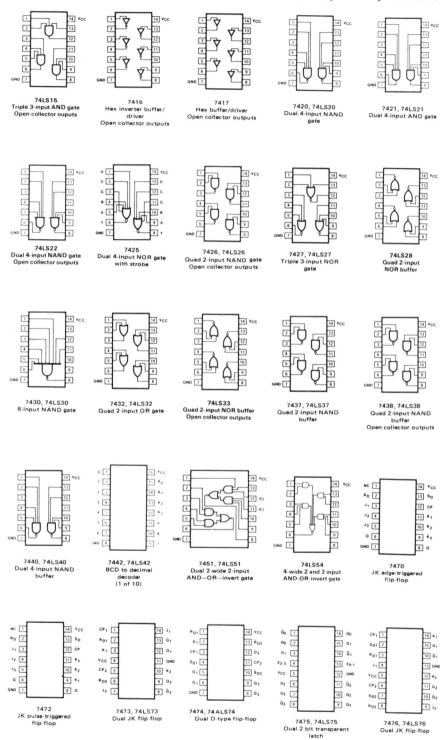

74LS15
Triple 3-input AND gate
Open collector ouputs

7416
Hex inverter buffer/
driver
Open collector outputs

7417
Hex buffer/driver
Open collector outputs

7420, 74LS20
Dual 4-input NAND
gate

7421, 74LS21
Dual 4-input AND gate

74LS22
Dual 4-input NAND gate
Open collector outputs

7425
Dual 4-input NOR gate
with strobe

7426, 74LS26
Quad 2-input NAND gate
Open collector outputs

7427, 74LS27
Triple 3-input NOR
gate

74LS28
Quad 2-input
NOR buffer

7430, 74LS30
8-input NAND gate

7432, 74LS32
Quad 2-input OR gate

74LS33
Quad 2-input NOR buffer
Open collector outputs

7437, 74LS37
Quad 2-input NAND
buffer

7438, 74LS38
Quad 2-input NAND
buffer
Open collector outputs

7440, 74LS40
Dual 4-input NAND
buffer

7442, 74LS42
BCD to decimal
decoder
(1 of 10)

7451, 74LS51
Dual 2-wide 2-input
AND—OR—invert gate

74LS54
4-wide 2 and 3 input
AND-OR-invert gate

7470
JK edge-triggered
flip-flop

7472
JK pulse-triggered
flip-flop

7473, 74LS73
Dual JK flip-flop

7474, 74ALS74
Dual D-type flip-flop

7475, 74LS75
Dual 2-bit transparent
latch

7476, 74LS76
Dual JK flip-flop

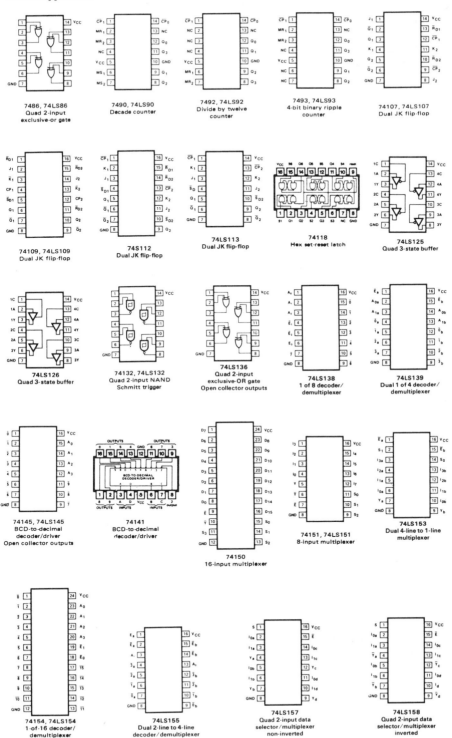

Appendix 5: Compatibility of projects

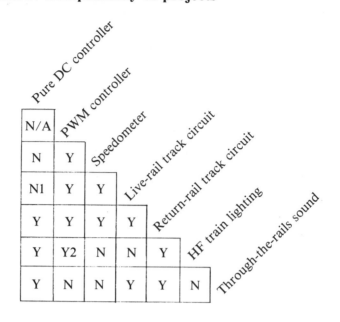

N/A   = Not normally used together
Y   = Compatible
N   = Not compatible
N1   = Not compatible unless through-the-rails sound *also* used
Y2   = HF lighting systems have been devised for use with PWM
        controllers, but the HF lighting system in Chapter 27 of this
        book is based on a pure DC controller.

Certain of the systems described in this book cannot be used with certain others. The above table summarises the main groups. Obviously if you insist upon having a certain facility, you may forfeit the possibility of having certain others, eg if you must have a speedometer, you cannot have HF train lighting or through-the-rails sound. (But you could have battery-backed train lighting and on-train-generated sound.) You just have to weigh up the pros and cons.

Appendix 6: Timers

CA555, CA555C Types

Timers

For Timing Delays & Oscillator Applications in
Commercial, Industrial, and Military Equipment

The RCA-CA555 and CA555C are highly
stable timers for use in precision timing and
oscillator applications. As timers, these
monolithic integrated circuits are capable of
producing accurate time delays for periods
ranging from microseconds through hours.
These devices are also useful for astable oscillator operation and can maintain an accurately controlled free-running frequency and
duty cycle with only two external resistors
and one capacitor.

The circuits of the CA555 and CA555C may
be triggered by the falling edge of the waveform signal, and the output of these circuits
can source or sink up to a 200-milliampere
current or drive TTL circuits.

The CA555 and CA555C are supplied in
hermetic IC Gold-CHIP 8-lead dual-in-line
plastic packages (G Suffix), standard 8-lead
TO-5 style packages (T suffix), 8-lead TO-5
style packages with dual-in-line formed leads
(DIL-CAN, S suffix), 8-lead dual-in-line plastic packages (MINI-DIP, E suffix), and in
chip form (H suffix). These types are direct
replacements for industry types in packages
with similar terminal arrangements e.g.SE555
and NE555, MC1555, and MC1455, respec
tively. The CA555 type circuits are intended
for applications requiring premium electrical
performance. The CA555C type circuits are
intended for applications requiring less stringent electrical characteristics.

MAXIMUM RATINGS, *Absolute-Maximum Values:*

```
DC SUPPLY VOLTAGE  . . .   18    V
DEVICE DISSIPATION:
  Up to T_A = 55°C . . . . .   600   mW
  Above T_A = 55°C Derate linearly   5  mW/°C
AMBIENT TEMPERATURE RANGE (All Types):
  Operating
  CA555  . . . . . . .  -55 to +125  °C
  CA555C . . . . . . .   0 to 70   °C▲
  Storage  . . . . . . .  -65 to +150  °C
LEAD TEMPERATURE (During Soldering):
  At distance 1/16" ± 1/32"
  (1.59 ± 0.79 mm) from case
  for 10 seconds max.  . . . .  +265   °C
```

CA555G, CA555CG:
  Hermetic Gold-CHIP 8-Lead Dual-In-Line
  Plastic Package (MINI-DIP)

CA555T, CA555CT:
  Standard 8-Lead TO-5 Style Package

CA555S, CA555CS:
  Standard 8-Lead TO-5 Style Package
  With Formed Leads (DIL-CAN)

CA555E, CA555CE:
  8-Lead Dual-In-Line Plastic Package
  (MINI-DIP)

Features:

- Accurate timing from microseconds
  through hours
- Astable and monostable operation
- Adjustable duty cycle
- Output capable of sourcing or sinking
  up to 200 mA
- Output capable of driving TTL devices
- Normally ON and OFF outputs
- High-temperature stability —0.005%/°C
- Directly interchangeable with SE555,
  NE555, MC1555, and MC1455

Applications:

- Precision timing
- Sequential timing
- Time-delay generation
- Pulse generation
- Pulse-width and position modulation
- Pulse detector

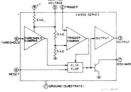

Fig. 1 — Functional diagram of the CA555
series.

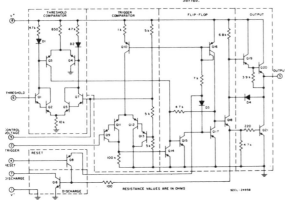

Fig. 2 — Schematic diagram of the CA555 and CA555C.

a. MINI-DIP plastic package
TO-5 style package with formed leads

b. TO-5 style package

Fig. 3 — Terminal assignment diagrams.

▲The CA555E, S, J, and T can be operated over the temperature range of —55°C to +125°C
although the published limits for certain electrical specifications apply only over the
temperature range of 0 to +70°C.

CA555, CA555C Types

ELECTRICAL CHARACTERISTICS, At $T_A = 25^oC$, $V^+ = 5$ to 15 V unless otherwise specified

CHARACTERISTIC	TEST CONDITIONS	LIMITS						UNITS
		CA555			CA555C			
		Min.	Typ.	Max.	Min.	Typ.	Max.	
DC Supply Voltage, V^+		4.5	–	18	4.5	–	16	V
DC Supply Current (Low State)*, I^+	$V^+ = 5$ V, $R_L = \infty$	–	3	5	–	3	6	mA
	$V^+ = 15$ V, $R_L = \infty$	–	10	12	–	10	15	mA
Threshold Voltage, V_{TH}		–	$(2/3)V^+$	–	–	$(2/3)V^+$	–	V
Trigger Voltage	$V^+ = 5$ V	1.45	1.67	1.9	–	1.67	–	V
	$V^+ = 15$ V	4.8	5	5.2	–	5	–	V
Trigger Current		–	0.5	–	–	0.5	–	µA
Threshold Current▲, I_{TH}		–	0.1	0.25	–	0.1	0.25	µA
Reset Voltage		0.4	0.7	1.0	0.4	0.7	1.0	V
Reset Current		–	0.1	–	–	0.1	–	mA
Control Voltage Level	$V^+ = 5$ V	2.9	3.33	3.8	2.6	3.33	4	V
	$V^+ = 15$ V	9.6	10	10.4	9	10	11	V
Output Voltage Drop: Low State, V_{OL}	$V^+ = 5$ V, $I_{SINK} = 5$ mA	–	–	–	–	0.25	0.35	V
	$I_{SINK} = 8$ mA	–	0.1	0.25	–	–	–	
	$V^+ = 15$ V, $I_{SINK} = 10$ mA	–	0.1	0.15	–	0.1	0.25	
	$I_{SINK} = 50$ mA	–	0.4	0.5	–	0.4	0.75	V
	$I_{SINK} = 100$ mA	–	2.0	2.2	–	2.0	2.5	
	$I_{SINK} = 200$ mA	–	2.5	–	–	2.5	–	
High State, V_{OH}	$V^+ = 5$ V, $I_{SOURCE} = 100$ mA	3.0	3.3	–	2.75	3.3	–	V
	$V^+ = 15$ V, $I_{SOURCE} = 100$ mA	13.0	13.3	–	12.75	13.3	–	
	$I_{SOURCE} = 200$ mA	–	12.5	–	–	12.5	–	
Timing Error (Monostable): Initial Accuracy	R_1, R_2 = 1 to 100 kΩ	–	0.5	2	–	1	–	%
Frequency Drift with Temperature	$C = 0.1$ µF Tested at $V^+ = 5$ V,	–	30	100	–	50	–	p/m/ ^{o}C
Drift with Supply Voltage	$V^+ = 15$ V	–	0.05	0.2	–	0.1	–	%/V
Output Rise Time, t_r		–	100	–	–	100	–	ns
Output Fall Time, t_f		–	100	–	–	100	–	ns

* When the output is in a high state, the dc supply current is typically 1 mA less than the low-state value.

▲ The threshold current will determine the sum of the values of R_1 and R_2 to be used in Fig. 16 (astable operation): the maximum total $R_1 + R_2 = 20$ MΩ.

Fig. 4 — Minimum pulse width vs. minimum trigger voltage.

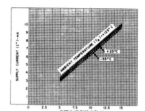

Fig. 5 — Supply current vs. supply voltage.

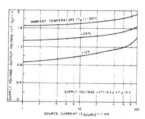

Fig. 6 — Output voltage drop (high state) vs. source current.

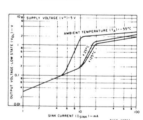

Fig. 7 — Output voltage-low state vs. sink current at $V^+ = 5$ V.

CA555, CA555C Types

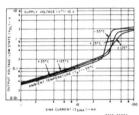

Fig.8 — Output voltage-low state vs. sink current at $V^+ = 10$ V.

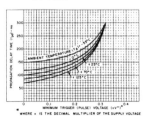

Fig.9 — Output voltage-low state vs. sink current at $V^+ = 15$ V.

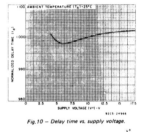

Fig.10 — Delay time vs. supply voltage.

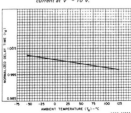

Fig.11 — Delay time vs. temperature.

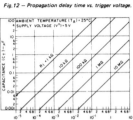

Fig.12 — Propagation delay time vs. trigger voltage.

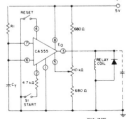

Fig.13 — Reset timer (monostable operation).

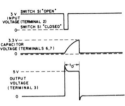

Fig.14 — Typical waveforms for reset timer.

Fig.15 — Time delay vs. resistance and capacitance.

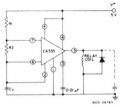

Fig.16 — Repeat cycle timer (astable operation).

TYPICAL APPLICATIONS

Reset Timer (Monostable Operation)

Fig.13 shows the CA555 connected as a reset timer. In this mode of operation capacitor C_T is initially held discharged by a transistor on the integrated circuit. Upon closing the "start" switch, or applying a negative trigger pulse to terminal 2, the integral timer flip-flop is "set" and releases the short circuit across C_T which drives the output voltage "high" (relay energized). The action allows the voltage across the capacitor to increase exponentially with the time constant $t = R_1C_T$. When the voltage across the capacitor equals 2/3 V^+, the comparator resets the flip-flop which in turn discharges the capacitor rapidly and drives the output to its low state.

Since the charge rate and threshold level of the comparator are both directly proportional to V^+, the timing interval is relatively independent of supply voltage variations. Typically, the timing varies only 0.05% for a 1 volt change in V^+.

Applying a negative pulse simultaneously to the reset terminal (4) and the trigger terminal (2) during the timing cycle discharges C_T and causes the timing cycle to restart. Momentarily closing only the reset switch during the timing interval discharges C_T, but the timing cycle does not restart.

Fig.14 shows the typical waveforms generated during this mode of operation, and Fig.15 gives the family of time delay curves with variations in R_1 and C_T.

Repeat Cycle Timer (Astable Operation)

Fig.16 shows the CA555 connected as a repeat cycle timer. In this mode of operation, the total period is a function of both R_1 and R_2;

$$T = 0.693(R_1 + 2R_2)C_T = t_1 + t_2$$

where $t_1 = 0.693(R_1 + R_2) C_T$
and $t_2 = 0.693(R_2)C_T$

The duty cycle is:

$$\frac{t_2}{t_1 + t_2} = \frac{R_2}{R_1 + 2R_2}$$

Typical waveforms generated during this mode of operation are shown in Fig. 17. Fig. 18 gives the family of curves of free running frequency with variations in the value of $(R_1 + 2R_2)$ and C_T.

CA555, CA555C Types

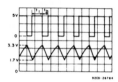

Top Trace: Output voltage (2V/div. and
0.5 ms/div.)
Bottom Trace: Capacitor voltage (1 V/
div. and 0.5 ms/div.)

*Fig. 17 — Typical waveforms for repeat
cycle timer.*

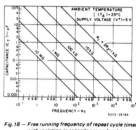

*Fig.18 — Free running frequency of repeat cycle timer
with variation in capacitance and resistance.*

Appendix 7: Operational Amplifiers

CA741, CA747, CA748, CA1458, CA1558 Types

Operational Amplifiers

High-Gain Single and Dual Operational Amplifiers
For Military, Industrial and Commercial Applications

The RCA-CA1458, CA1558 (dual types); CA741C, CA741 (single-types); CA747C, CA747 (dual types); and CA748C, CA748 (single types) are general-purpose, high-gain operational amplifiers for use in military, industrial, and commercial applications.

These monolithic silicon integrated-circuit devices provide output short-circuit protection and latch-free operation. These types also feature wide common-mode and differential-mode signal ranges and have low-offset voltage nulling capability when used with an appropriately valued potentiometer. A 5-megohm potentiometer is used for offset nulling types CA748C, CA748 (See Fig. 10); a 10-kilohm potentiometer is used for offset nulling types CA741C, CA741, CA747CE, CA747CG, CA747E, CA747G (See Fig. 9); and types CA1458, CA1558, CA747CT, have no specific terminals for offset nulling. Each type consists of a differential-input amplifier that effectively drives a gain and level-shifting stage having a complementary emitter-follower output.

This operational amplifier line also offers the circuit designer the option of operation with internal or external phase compensation.

Types CA748C and CA748, which are externally phase compensated (terminals 1 and 8) permit a choice of operation for improved bandwidth and slew-rate capabilities. Unity gain with external phase compensation can be obtained with a single 30-pF capacitor. All the other types are internally phase-compensated.

RCA's manufacturing process makes it possible to produce IC operational amplifiers with low-burst ("popcorn") noise characteristics. Type CA6741, a low-noise version of the CA741, gives limit specifications for burst noise in the data bulletin, File No. 530. Contact your RCA Sales Representative for information pertinent to other operational amplifier types that meet low-burst noise specifications.

"G" Suffix Types—Hermetic Gold-CHIP in Dual-In-Line Plastic Package
"E" Suffix Types—Standard Dual-In-Line Plastic Package
"T" and "S" Suffix Types—TO-5 Style Package

Features:

■ Input bias current (all types): 500 nA max.
■ Input offset current (all types): 200 nA max.

Applications:

■ Comparator
■ DC amplifier
■ Integrator or differentiator
■ Multivibrator
■ Narrow-band or band-pass filter
■ Summing amplifier

1a.—CA741CS, CA741CT, CA741S, & CA741T with internal phase compensation.

1b.—CA747CT and CA747T with internal phase compensation.

1c.—CA748CS, CA748CT, CA748S, and CA748T with external phase compensation.

Fig. 1 — Functional diagrams.

MAXIMUM RATINGS, *Absolute-Maximum Values at* $T_A = 25°C$:

DC Supply Voltage (between V⁺ and V⁻ terminals):	
CA741C, CA747C▲, CA748C, CA1458▲	36 V
CA741, CA747▲, CA748, CA1558▲	44 V
Differential Input Voltage	±30 V
DC Input Voltage*	±15 V
Output Short-Circuit Duration.	Indefinite
Device Dissipation:	
Up to 70°C (CA741C, CA748C)	500 mW
Up to 75°C (CA741, CA748)	500 mW
Up to 30°C (CA747)	800 mW
Up to 25°C (CA747C)	800 mW
Up to 30°C (CA1558)	680 mW
Up to 25°C (CA1458)	680 mW
For Temperatures Indicated Above . . . . Derate linearly 6.67 mW/°C	
Voltage between Offset Null and V⁻ (CA741C, CA741, CA747CE, CA747CG).	±0.5 V
Ambient Temperature Range:	
Operating – CA741, CA747E, CA748, CA1558.	−55 to +125 °C
CA741C, CA747C, CA748C, CA1458	0 to +70 °C†
Storage	−65 to +150 °C
Lead Temperature (During Soldering):	
At distance 1/16 ± 1/32 inch (1.59 ± 0.79 mm) from case for 10 seconds max.	265 °C

* If Supply Voltage is less than ± 15 volts, the Absolute Maximum Input Voltage is equal to the Supply Voltage.

▲ Voltage values apply for each of the dual operational amplifiers.

† All types in any package style can be operated over the temperature range of −55 to +125°C, although the published limits for certain electrical specifications apply only over the temperature range of 0 to +70°C.

Reprinted by permission of RCA Corporation, Solid State Division. Copyright 1977 by RCA Corporation.

CA741, CA747, CA748, CA1458, CA1558 Types

RCA Type No.	No. of Ampl.	Phase Comp.	Offset Voltage Null	Min. A_{OL}	Max. V_{IO} (mV)	Operating-Temperature Range (°C)
CA1458	dual	int.	no	20k	6	0 to +70▲
CA1558	dual	int.	no	50k	5	−55 to +125
CA741C	single	int.	yes	20k	6	0 to +70▲
CA741	single	int.	yes	50k	5	−55 to +125
CA747C	dual	int.	yes*	20k	6	0 to +70▲
CA747	dual	int.	yes*	50k	5	−55 to +125
CA748C	single	ext.	yes	20k	6	0 to +70▲
CA748	single	ext.	yes	50k	5	−55 to +125

*In the 14-lead dual-in-line plastic package only.

▲All types in any package style can be operated over the temperature range of −55 to +125°C, although the published limits for certain electrical specifications apply only over the temperature range of 0 to +70°C.

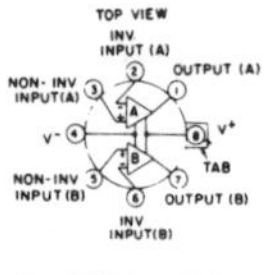

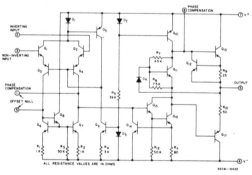

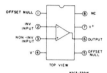

1d.–CA1458S,CA1458T,CA1558S, and CA1558T and internal phase compensation.

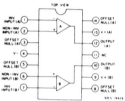

1e.–CA741CE,CA741CG,CA741E, and CA741G with internal phase compensation.

ORDERING INFORMATION

When ordering any of these types, it is important that the appropriate suffix letter for the package required be affixed to the type number. For example: If a CA1458 in a straight-lead TO-5 style package is desired, order CA1458T.

Type No.	PACKAGE TYPE AND SUFFIX LETTER										FIG. No.
	TO-5 STYLE			PLASTIC		Gold-CHIP PLASTIC		CHIP	Gold-CHIP	BEAM-LEAD	
	8L	10L	DIL-CAN	8L	14L	8L	14L				
CA1458	T		S	E		G		H	GH		1d, 1h
CA1558	T		S	E		G					1d, 1h
CA741C	T		S	E		G		H	GH		1a, 1e
CA741	T		S	E		G				L	1a, 1e
CA747C		T			E		G	H	GH		1b, 1f
CA747		T			E		G				1b, 1f
CA748C	T		S	E		G		H	GH		1c, 1g
CA748	T		S	E		G					1c, 1g

1f.–CA747CE,CA747CG,CA747E, and CA747G with internal phase compensation.

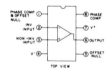

1g.–CA748CE,CA748CG,CA748E, and CA748G with external phase compensation.

Fig.2–Schematic diagram of operational amplifier with external phase compensation for CA748C and CA748.

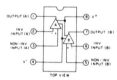

1h.–CA1458E,CA1458G,CA1558E, and CA1558G with internal phase compensation.

Fig. 1 – Functional Diagrams (Cont'd)

CA741, CA747, CA748, CA1458, CA1558 Types

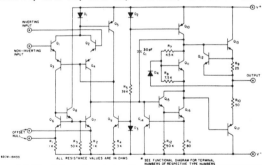

Fig.3—Schematic diagram of operational amplifiers with internal phase compensation for CA741C, CA741, and for each amplifier of the CA747C, CA747, CA1458, and CA1558.

ELECTRICAL CHARACTERISTICS
For Equipment Design

CHARACTERISTIC	TEST CONDITIONS Supply Voltage, $V^+ = 15$ V, $V^- = -15$ V	Ambient Temperature, T_A	CA741 CA747* CA748 CA1558* Min.	Typ.	Max.	UNITS
Input Offset Voltage, V_{IO}	$R_S = \leqslant 10\,k\Omega$	25 °C	–	1	5	mV
		–55 to +125 °C	–	1	6	
Input Offset Current, I_{IO}		25 °C	–	20	200	nA
		–55 °C	–	85	500	
		+125 °C	–	7	200	
Input Bias Current, I_{IB}		25 °C	–	80	500	nA
		–55 °C	–	300	1500	
		+125 °C	–	30	500	
Input Resistance, R_I			0.3	2	–	$M\Omega$
Open-Loop Differential Voltage Gain, A_{OL}	$R_L \geqslant 2\,k\Omega$ $V_O = \pm 10$ V	25 °C	50,000	200,000	–	
		–55 to +125 °C	25,000	–		
Common-Mode Input Voltage Range, V_{ICR}		–55 to +125 °C	±12	±13	–	V
Common-Mode Rejection Ratio, CMRR	$R_S \leqslant 10\,k\Omega$	–55 to +125 °C	70	90	–	dB
Supply Voltage Rejection Ratio, PSRR	$R_S \leqslant 10\,k\Omega$	–55 to +125 °C	–	30	150	$\mu V/V$
Output Voltage Swing, V_{OPP}	$R_L \geqslant 10\,k\Omega$	–55 to +125 °C	±12	±14	–	V
	$R_L \geqslant 2\,k\Omega$	–55 to +125 °C	±10	±13	–	
Supply Current, $I^\pm$		25 °C	–	1.7	2.8	mA
		–55 °C	–	2	3.3	
		+125 °C	–	1.5	2.5	
Device Dissipation, P_D		25 °C	–	50	85	mW
		–55 °C	–	60	100	
		+125 °C	–	45	75	

* Values apply for each section of the dual amplifiers.

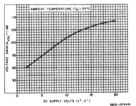

Fig.4—Open-loop voltage gain vs. supply voltage for all types except CA748 and CA748C.

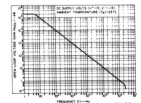

Fig.5—Open-loop voltage gain vs. frequency for all types except CA748 and CA748C.

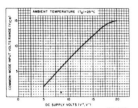

Fig.6—Common-mode input voltage range vs. supply voltage for all types.

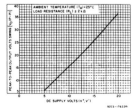

Fig.7—Peak-to-peak output voltage vs. supply voltage for all types except CA748 and CA748C.

CA741, CA747, CA748, CA1458, CA1558 Types

ELECTRICAL CHARACTERISTICS
For Equipment Design

CHARACTERISTIC	TEST CONDITIONS Supply Voltage, V^+ = 15 V, V^- = −15 V		LIMITS CA741C CA747C* CA748C CA1458*			UNITS
		Ambient Temperature, T_A	Min.	Typ.	Max.	
Input Offset Voltage, V_{IO}	$R_S = \leqslant 10\,k\Omega$	25 °C	−	2	6	mV
		0 to 70 °C	−	−	7.5	
Input Offset Current, I_{IO}		25 °C	−	20	200	nA
		0 to 70 °C	−	−	300	
Input Bias Current, I_{IB}		25 °C	−	80	500	nA
		0 to 70 °C	−	−	800	
Input Resistance, R_I			0.3	2	−	$M\Omega$
Open-Loop Differential Voltage Gain, A_{OL}	$R_L \geqslant 2\,k\Omega$ $V_O = \pm 10$ V	25 °C	20,000	200,000	−	
		0 to 70 °C	15,000	−	−	
Common-Mode Input Voltage Range, V_{ICR}		25 °C	±12	±13	−	V
Common-Mode Rejection Ratio, CMRR	$R_S \leqslant 10\,k\Omega$	25 °C	70	90	−	dB
Supply-Voltage Rejection Ratio, PSRR	$R_S \leqslant 10\,k\Omega$	25 °C	−	30	150	$\mu V/V$
Output Voltage Swing, V_{OPP}	$R_L \geqslant 10\,k\Omega$	25 °C	±12	±14	−	
	$R_L \geqslant 2\,k\Omega$	25 °C	±10	±13	−	V
		0 to 70 °C	±10	±13	−	
Supply Current, $I^\pm$		25 °C	−	1.7	2.8	mA
Device Dissipation, P_D		25 °C	−	50	85	mW

* Values apply for each section of the dual amplifiers.

ELECTRICAL CHARACTERISTICS
Typical Values Intended Only for Design Guidance

CHARACTERISTIC	TEST CONDITIONS $V\pm$ = ±15 V	TYP. VALUES ALL TYPES	UNITS
Input Capacitance, C_I		1.4	pF
Offset Voltage Adjustment Range		±15	mV
Output Resistance, R_O		75	Ω
Output Short-Circuit Current		25	mA
Transient Response: Rise Time, t_r	Unity gain V_I = 20 mV	0.3	μs
Overshoot	R_L = 2 kΩ $C_L \leqslant 100$ pF	5	%
Slew Rate, SR: Closed-loop	$R_L \geqslant 2\,k\Omega$	0.5	V/μs
Open-loop▲		40	

▲ Open-loop slew rate applies only for types CA748C and CA748.

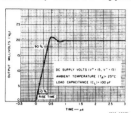

Fig.8—Output voltage vs. transient response time for CA741C and CA741

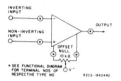

Fig.9—Voltage-offset null circuit for CA741C, CA741, CA747CE, CA747CG, CA747E, and CA747G.

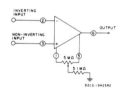

Fig.10—Voltage-offset null circuit for CA748C and CA748.

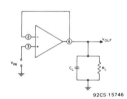

Fig.11—Transient response test circuit for all types.

Epilogue

The future

I trust that this book has given you some ideas for electronic projects for use on your (or your club's) layout and, in particular, I hope that it has opened your eyes to the huge potential of digital systems. Practically nothing is impossible.

Someone will surely say, what about computers? Why have I not mentioned the uses of computers (the ultimate digital systems) on model railways? The answer is that in eight years of model railway electronics experience, I have not found any application in which a computer would help. Actually, this is not quite true. The progressive cab control system described in Chapter 26 was first conceived as a computer program. I discussed it with many computer experts and asked for advice on how to implement it. It was a very long program, they told me, would need floppy disc storage and I should need a complex interface unit to 'match' the computer output to the railway. Indeed, as someone pointed out, the interface unit would be so complex that, with a couple of minor alterations, it could do the job on its own — so, no need for the computer! It is, if you like, a computer project which ends with you 'taking away the computer you first thought of'. This is the system described in Chapter 26. Thus, I repeat, I have not yet found any model railway application for a computer, but, not so very long ago, I wrote almost identical words about ICs and then I wrote this book! So perhaps in a few years' time I shall find myself writing a book entitled *Computer Projects for Railway Modellers,* or suchlike.

Computers are not the only high-technology product having model railway potential. A video recording of a busy city street with bustling pedestrians and queues of cars, taxis and buses could be replayed on a monitor behind your main station to give a moving backscene! On-train TV cameras that simulate you sitting in the cab and looking along the line stretching out in advance of you were just one innovation mentioned in the humorous article '2001' by Ron Stewien (*Railway Modeller,* December 1981). Many a true word is spoken, or even written, in jest and many of Mr Stewien's ideas are feasible *now*.

There has been talk of the use of holography to give fully three-dimensional background scenics. With a reflection hologram (which can be used flat against a solid wall and illuminated from in front) you can get a 'depth' of about 1 metre but the two main drawbacks are (i) expense and (ii) that the holograms are monochrome, ie of a single colour.

So, obviously, the future holds techniques in store for us which are sometimes beyond our wildest dreams. I am confident that in the year 2000 there will be plenty of active railway modellers using not only the best traditional techniques but also taking advantage of the best that the new technology has to offer. Readers who are interested in such new developments — and also in more down-to-earth electronic projects — are recommended to the quarterly magazine *Model Railway Electronics* published by Dalkeith Publishing, Kettering, Northants.

Index

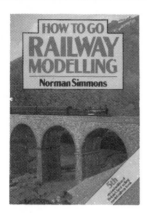

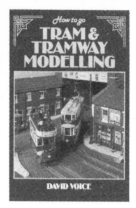

Other PSL books for railway modellers

How to Go Railway Modelling
(5th edition)
by Norman Simmons
All you need to know in order to enjoy the absorbing hobby of railway
modelling is here in this best-selling book. Now in its fifth revised, updated
edition and, as ever, a thoroughly practical handbook for all ages.

Practical Electronics for Railway Modellers 1
by Roger Amos
Railway modelling has really benefited from the electronics revolution. Here,
through a series of fascinating projects, the modeller can learn how to make
extensive and useful improvements to his layout, and bring it bang up to date.

PSL's Practical Guide to Railway Modelling
edited by Michael Andress
This good-value practical handbook comprises a variety of railway modelling
topics chosen to be of greatest use to the modeller with no special skill or
experience. All the features have been selected to cover the main aspects of
railway modelling—locomotives, passenger and goods rolling stock, special
equipment, operation, structures and scenery.

How To Go Tram & Tramway Modelling
by David Voice
This is the first full-length treatment of an increasingly popular aspect of the
modelling hobby. In clear text accompanied by numerous photographs and
diagrams, the author explains everything which the would-be tram modeller needs
to know, while long and detailed appendices provide a great deal of valuable
information not available anywhere else.

See also back jacket flap.